SECRET
UNDERGROUND
CORSHAM

by

Nick McCamley

FOLLY BOOKS

Published in 2021 by
Folly Books Ltd
Monkton Farleigh
BA15 2QP
www.follybooks.co.uk

ISBN 978-1-9161789-4-6

Designed and Typeset by Vicky

Printed and bound in England by Corsham Print Ltd.

PREFACE

This book was written to provide a comprehensive overview of the quite incredible subterranean world that lies beneath Corsham and the surrounding areas. A number of specialist books have been published over the previous decade or so by Folly Books, recording in words and pictures the detailed history of Corsham's underground infrastructure, including Derek Hawkins' *Bath Stone Quarries*, Nick Catford's *Burlington* and the current author's *Secret Underground Cities* and *Second World War Secret Bunkers*.

This book, however, brings all of these previous tomes together into a single, easily digestible volume which, I hope, will be of interest to those readers who don't need to know all the financial intricacies of the Victorian quarrying companies, the engineering and geological difficulties encountered and overcome during the adaptation of many of the quarries for ammunition storage (and other purposes) during the Second World War, or the geo-political shenanigans and rampant paranoia that led to the construction of the Burlington bunker. What we have here is a good, overall history, profusely illustrated, of all the major features and developments of the Corsham quarries from the 1830s to the present day. Over the years many myths and urban legends have circulated regarding what exactly went on beneath Corsham - here the reader will discover that many of those legends were closer to the truth than they ever imagined.....

Corsham appears to be growing at an exponential rate, with new housing developments springing up like mushrooms overnight. With luck, this book will enlighten these new residents as to what lies beneath their feet and explain why, for instance, a monstrous concrete monolith looms menacingly over Copenacre Way, squatting in a sinister fashion beside the A4 western approach to the town.

A further reason for writing this book is that Derek Hawkins' *Bath Stone Quarries* and Nick Catford's *Burlington* are currently out of print and although a reprint is scheduled, the current vagaries of exchange rates and shipping delays mean that they may be some time coming. With luck, this book may stimulate sufficient interest for the reader to thirst for further knowledge, a thirst that in time Derek and Nick's books will quench.

The vast majority of the illustrations in this book, with the exception perhaps of those of Monkton Farleigh quarry, were taken by, or come from the collection of, Derek Hawkins, and in many ways this book is as much his work as it is mine, and for that reason I express my deep gratitude to him. Nick Catford too, has supplied me with some great photographs and, indeed, has always shown the greatest generosity in allowing the use of his photographs in other books published by Folly Books.

Although almost all of the once highly secretive underground government facilities in the Corsham area are now long abandoned, a handful of small installations remain; although what goes on in them is supposed to be more-or-less secret their locations are not so secret but, as we have no photographs to illustrate them, they have been excluded from this book.

Nick McCamley
Monkton Farleigh
September 2021

CONTENTS

MONKS PARK QUARRY
Inclined entrance shaft

SECTION 1

THE QUARRIES

Corsham initially owed its wealth and status to the woolen trade, but as this industry declined in Southern England towards the end of the eighteenth and into the nineteenth century, it was replaced, by a fortuitous coincidence of events, by the stone-quarrying industry, which arguably has, for almost two hundred years, been the single most important factor in the evolution of the town and the surrounding villages. The quarries that lie beneath Corsham are known throughout the world and have huge national and international significance. Not only did they produce stone for the building of some of the most monumental and magnificent buildings across the globe, the quarries became a key element in securing Britain's safety in the Second World War, and they provided (and to some extent continue still to provide) key emergency government control and communications facilities throughout the Cold War and beyond.

A VERY BRIEF HISTORY

Although the local stone is reputed to have been quarried for building purposes since at least Roman times it was not until the nineteenth century that it became a true commercial industry with stone extracted on a speculative basis in the hope of finding a commercial market. Previous to that, stone tended to be quarried for specific purposed – usually by the landowner for the building or extension of a great house or an ecclesiastical building or perhaps for smaller agricultural buildings or workers' cottages. The key thing was that stone tended to be cut from close to where it was needed. The deeds for properties in Limpley Stoke, for example, where the author once lived, specify that the houses should be built from stone quarried from their own grounds, and houses on the steep northern hillside of Bradford-on-Avon on Tory and Middle Rank are built on the shelved open quarries from which the stone for their own construction was taken. One factor that held back the quarrying industry in the Corsham area was that the transport infrastructure was very poor. Oolitic limestone is an enormously heavy material and transporting it over long distances, particularly over the very inadequate roads and tracks that existed, made transport to distant markets prohibitively difficult and expensive. By comparison, the quarries around Bath and Bradford-on-Avon enjoyed a temporary advantage from the fact that they were close to the River Avon (and by the end of the eighteenth century to the

7

Kennet & Avon canal), which eased the transport problem to some degree.

Things suddenly changed, however, with the construction of Box railway tunnel by the Great Western Railway. The alignment of the tunnel, at around 80 – 100 feet below ground, cut through the stratum of Oolitic limestone and at once revealed the true extent of the vast reserves of superb building stone in the Box and Corsham area. Perhaps as important as the discovery of the quantity readily available was the fact that the railways provided the means of distributing large, heavy and otherwise unwieldy quantities of stone easily, cheaply and very quickly throughout the country and, via the rail-linked ports, to distant lands where Corsham stone's already growing reputation for aesthetic beauty and ease of working made it the go-to material for the most prestigious corporate, state and public buildings.

Such was the demand for Box and Corsham stone that by 1850 it was said that the working man (and the greater part of the population at that time was working class), had two choices: they could either work on the land as agricultural labourers, or they could work under the land as quarry labourers. Over the following thirty years the industry grew exponentially and by the mid 1870s there were dozens of small and medium sized quarrying firms at work in North Wiltshire, all engaged in an aggressive price-war that pushed down prices to the extent that many were faced with the prospect of imminent bankruptcy. It was obvious that this state of affairs could not continue, and in 1887, under the impetus of Cornelius Pictor, one of Corsham's most prominent quarrymen, several of the largest quarrying firms in the area combined to form The Bath Stone Firms Ltd. The original members of the firm were: Stone Brothers Ltd, Randell, Saunders & Company Ltd, Corsham Bath Stone Company Ltd, Pictor & Sons, Isaac Sumsion, and S. R. Noble. The only large producer in the Corsham area to trade outside the Bath Stone Firms Ltd was the Yockney and Hartham Park Stone Company, which remained independent until 1939. Just over a decade later, in 1899, the firm took control of the Portland quarries and in 1911 changed its name to the Bath & Portland Stone Firms Ltd. Shortly before the start of the Second World War, the quarries at Beer, Ham Hill, Doulting and Clipsham were added to the firm's portfolio, giving them a virtual monopoly in the supply of oolitic limestone to the building trade.

After a century of continued growth the 1930s heralded a change in the fortunes of the Bath & Portland Stone Firms, particularly in the Corsham quarries. Throughout the good times the firm had benefited from low wage rates and an abundance of cheap labour, but since the end of the First World War wages generally had been increasing and employment opportunities widening, which made the prospect of working in the quarries, even with recession looming, seem increasingly uncongenial. Although the stone reserves were far from exhausted, the best and most economically worked stone had been extracted by the mid-1930s and consequently marginal costs were rising, and all this was occurring at the beginning of the worst financial catastrophe in modern times. In a recession the first sector to suffer is the construction industry, and if no houses, factories or public buildings are being erected then there is no demand for building materials and the quarrying industry suffers in consequence. By 1931 the Bath and Portland Stone Firm's home and export markets had collapsed and the company found itself burdened with bills for dead-rents on unproductive quarries and leases payable on worked-out quarries and on stone reserves earmarked for future exploitation but upon which there seemed little likelihood of quick returns.

Some relief was offered from an unexpected quarter in 1934, however, when the War Office offered to purchase many of the company's abandoned quarries. By 1934 the British government knew another European war was inevitable, although there was some vagueness as to when the crisis might occur. The general consensus, however, was that the very early 1940s might be the trigger point. At that time the threat of air-power was beginning to dominate the fears of Britain's strategic planners who, based upon grossly erroneous over-estimations of the German air-force, concluded that on the day war was declared the skies over London would blacken with enemy bombers, the capital would be bombed to oblivion, it would be the end of England, the end of the Empire, and Germany would henceforth rule the world. On a lighter note, though, they concluded that whilst Germany had an overwhelming numerical superiority in aircraft, those aircraft had a limited range and could fly no further than London and south-east England. Thus, although London and the Home Counties might be wiped from the map, the rest of Britain would remain unscathed. Unfortunately, the British army's considerable war reserves of ammunition were stored in unprotected surface buildings at Woolwich Arsenal and at Bramley near Basingstoke, both of which were well within the estimated range of the Luftwaffe bombers.

So, adopting a belt-and-braces approach, the War Office decided that new accommodation for these stocks should be found west of a notional line drawn from the Wash to the Solent (and thus in the safe areas of Britain) and, to be doubly sure, insisted that this accommodation should be underground. It was the search for suitable and available underground space that in November 1934 led to the inspection of Ridge quarry at Neston by Major Minnis and a team of Royal Engineers officers. The following year Ridge quarry was purchased by the War Office. Between then and the end of 1937 three more much larger quarries at Monkton Farleigh, Tunnel, and Eastlays were subsequently acquired and, over a four-year period and at vast expense, converted into highly sophisticated underground ammunition magazines known collectively as Central Ammunition Depot Corsham. Several other smaller quarries were taken over by the Air Ministry and the Ministry of Supply for similar storage uses. In November 1940, as a response to concerted German attacks upon Britain's aircraft factories, all the remaining Bath and Portland quarries in north-west Wiltshire were requisition by the Ministry of Aircraft Production for conversion into underground factories and warehouses. The largest of these, the 3,000,000 square-foot Spring quarry at Corsham, was adapted as an engine factory for the Bristol Aeroplane Company and was to become the largest underground factory in the world. Government ownership of the quarries during the war years affected profoundly the unique state in which the majority of them survive today. By the latter part of 1938 all except perhaps three or four of the quarries (Spring, Monk's Park and Limpley Stoke quarries being the principal exceptions) had ceased work and were under government control. By November 1940 all of the remainder had stopped production and remained in government hands for at least a decade after hostilities ended.

Quarries earmarked for the Ministry of Aircraft Production were peremptorily requisitioned on the afternoon of Saturday 7 December 1940 and the quarrymen told not to return to work on the following Monday. Mark Pictor, Chairman of the Bath and Portland Stone Company, wrote to his land-agent:

On Saturday the District Valuer arrived at our office and requisitioned the whole of our Bath Stone quarries with the exception of Monk's Park, which had been requisitioned a few days earlier by the Admiralty … This has come as something of a surprise to us as we did not anticipate the Ministry stepping in at all … As you can imagine we are left rather high and dry, but I suppose we shall hear something this week. In the meantime of course it is difficult to know what to do with the men as I do not want to disperse them knowing how difficult it will be getting them back again, but with all the quarries requisitioned it leaves very little work to which we can put them.

On the last day workmen, not knowing that they would never return, left behind personal effects, tasks uncompleted and tools still in position. Where the quarries were converted for military occupation or for use as war factories, all this was of course swept away, but in those sections of the workings which were found unsuitable for conversion these artifacts remained untouched. Indeed, in areas contiguous with those sections of quarries which remained in government hands until the early twenty-first century the artifacts have survived in pristine condition for more than sixty years. The result of this, from the point of view of an industrial archaeologist, is that what still survives is essentially a pre-war industry preserved in aspic, a series of perfect little subterranean time capsules. But it is even better than that. Because the Bath and Portland Stone Firm always had access to a ready supply of cheap labour it was never presented with any incentive to modernise or mechanise, so the tools and working practices employed underground in 1938 were little changed from those employed in

1838. Indeed, even the quarrymen's dress was similar and it is often difficult to date old photographs accurately to within half a century. So, what survives now is in many respects a fairly accurate reflection of the quarrying industry in the mid-nineteenth century.

The most profound change in working practices occurred after the war when the first few quarries were released by the government. In the new social and economic climate of the post-war world it was obvious that the stone industry would never be the same again, rising costs and competition from new materials, particularly pre-stressed reinforced concrete, were making natural stone uncompetitive except for renovation work and for the most prestigious new projects. There was a brief resurgence in the company's fortunes to meet the demands of post-war reconstruction but thereafter demand continued to decline. During the wartime conversion work, the War Office had brought in tens of thousands of unemployed colliery men from the distressed areas of the north-east. These men brought with them their expertise in the use of mechanised coal mining equipment and by 1938 experiments were under way at Corsham using coal cutting machinery adapted by the Royal Engineers to cope with the different characteristics of the local stone. Electric and pneumatic semi-rotary arc-shearers were tested, with only moderate success, but two types of chain coal-cutters, the Dreadnought machine supplied by Anderson, Boyes & Company of Glasgow, and Mavor & Coulson's Samson coal-cutter, proved highly effective and several were subsequently purchased for work in the quarries. The Bath & Portland directors were obviously impressed by the performance of these machines because they acquired three from Mavor & Coulson and began tests with them in Moor Park quarry in 1948. An earlier attempt at partial mechanisation using semi-rotary drills yielded less than sparkling results, but the Samsons, despite the fact that substantial amounts of stone were lost due to the great width of the cutting blade, were far more satisfactory.

So successful were they that Samson and Dreadnought machines, many of them manufactured in the late 1930s, became the staple devices for cutting stone in the Corsham quarries well into the twenty-first century. Since the 1980s, however, more modern, lighter-weight machines based upon the chain cutter principle but using hydraulic rather than electric power and with more sophisticated control systems, have gradually displaced the earlier machines in the former Bath & Portland (now Hanson Minerals) quarries. Both here and in the Bath Stone Company's quarry at Limpley Stoke other methods of stone cutting, including chain drilling with pneumatic drills, or drilling as an adjunct to hand-sawing, have also been used with some success. The only quarries currently operating in the Corsham area are Park Lane quarry and Hartham Park quarry at Pickwick where the discovery of a hitherto unknown bed of Box ground stone has secured its future for some years.

TOOLS, EQUIPMENT & METHODS

The earliest quarry workings occurred where the limestone strata outcropped on hillside edges. There the stone was generally most fractured and thus could be extracted with the most primitive of tools and the minimum of effort. These were supplemented some time later by 'hole' quarries which consisted of excavations distant from the valley outcrops where the surface of the ground was opened up to expose the stone below. As we have noted above, this technique had two major drawbacks in that, firstly, it involved the loss of good agricultural land and, secondly, it became uneconomic as the depth of overburden that needed to be removed to reach the stone increased. Both of these difficulties could be overcome at suitable locations by driving horizontal or gently inclined tunnels or adits into the hillside more or less on the level of the limestone beds, and extracting the stone from underground. Examples of this sort of quarry can be found at Kingsdown, Westwood, Bradford-on-Avon, and on the northern perimeters of the hillsides at Box and Farleigh Down.

From the early years of the nineteenth century stone was being extracted from depths in excess of eighty feet via vertical shaft quarries at locations some distance from the valley edges. The earliest recorded vertical shaft is at Travelers' Rest quarry at Pickwick, sunk around 1810, while the most spectacular is the Cathedral quarry on Box Hill, sunk by Job Pictor in 1829 and worked over a period of some twenty years. At least four other vertical winding shaft quarries were established in the Bath and Corsham area, including Hudswell, South Wraxall, Sheep Drove quarry at Monkton Farleigh and Coxe's shaft on Combe Down. After 1845 most new quarries were accessed via slope-shafts, inclined from the surface at 30-45 degrees, an innovation concurrent with the introduction of narrow-gauge tramways underground. The inclined shafts enabled loaded wagons to be drawn up from underground by means of horse-gins, steam winches, gas engines or, later in the twentieth century, diesel or electric winches. The first inclined shaft appears to have been sunk at Tunnel quarry in 1845 by Randell, Saunders & Company.

Over the following half-century a further twenty-five slope-shafts were sunk into new or existing quarries, the last being completed in 1908 at Copenacre quarry to replace an existing vertical shaft. A rash of new, inclined shaft quarries were sunk around the turn of the nineteenth and twentieth centuries, the majority on land belonging to the Neston Estate. Many of them proved unsuccessful. The normal procedure was to sink a vertical trial shaft to a depth of approximately eighty feet to prove the strata and then to excavate an incline about two hundred yards distant, working towards the trial bore which would eventually serve as a ventilation shaft for the quarry. The predominant cause of so many of these later ventures to be failures appears to have been over-

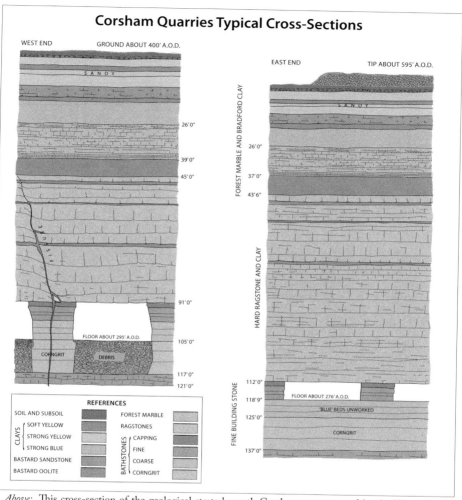

Corsham Quarries Typical Cross-Sections

Above: This cross-section of the geological strata beneath Corsham was prepared by the War Office in 1936 in preparation for the conversion of the quarry workings into an ammunition storage depot. This shows the east and west ends of Tunnel Quarry, but is fairly typical of all the quarries in the Corsham area.

optimistic evaluations of the stone found in the trial shafts. From the very beginning the quarrymen took advantage of the natural faulting of the stone to ease the process of extraction.

We have already seen that the various strata of oolitic limestone lie in a series of contiguous beds of various thicknesses to a total depth of approximately thirty feet. Within these beds the stone is fractured by a series of horizontal joints that trend in a north-east to south-west direction. These primary joints are intersected randomly by lateral fissures running at ninety degrees to them.

The quarrymen always attempted to dig their headings along the joint lines, thus obviating the need to cut the stone on at least one side of the working face. The method of extraction varied slightly from quarry to quarry and developed over time, but the essential principles remained the same. In the earliest workings, a hand pick or jadding bar was used to cut a narrow slot or 'jad' into the width of the working face, immediately below the bed of stone that was to be removed. The jad was approximately eight inches in height and as deep into the face (usually four to six feet) as the required dimension of the finished block. Next, a vertical jad of similar dimension would be cut into the face about a metre from the left-hand wall (assuming the left wall followed a natural joint) to allow room for the required block of stone to be severed from the face by means of wedges hammered into the joint. Further blocks to the right could now be removed by cutting more vertical jads at suitable spacings and picking the back of the block.

By the 1840s large, deep-bladed steel hand saws or 'frigbobs' were being introduced into the quarries in order to speed up the process of stone cutting at the face. The process adopted when using saws was a modification of the earlier method; first, a jad was picked across the width of the working face just below roof level, of a sufficient height to enable a shallow-bladed saw (generally a worn-down frigbob), to be used to start a downward, vertical cut through the upper bed of stone. Once the cut was of sufficient depth the small saw or

Below: Picking the jad just below quarry roof level to make space for the shallow saw or 'razzer' used to start the vertical cuts in the stone face.

Left: With the picking bed or 'jad' complete, the sawyer can now begin the first down ward cut with the shallow-bladed razzer.

'razzer' was replaced by a much sturdier, deep-bladed frigbob and the cut was continued downwards to the bedding plane. A second vertical cut was then made approximately thirty inches from the first. Both cuts were tapered slightly inwards to the back of the cut in order to prevent the block jamming when it was pulled out. Two or three sets of plug and feather wedges were then inserted into pockets chiseled into the line of the horizontal joint between the beds and hammered home. The objective was to split the block away from the face at its back end. This stage completed, a dovetail slot approximately nine inches deep was cut in the front of the block to facilitate the insertion of a three-piece Lewis-bolt to which a chain or wire rope would be attached and a crane used to pull the block from the face. Often, the block would not break away from the face cleanly and much work would be required to square-up the face using picks. Once the first block, or 'wrist' stone, was removed a quarryman would climb into the cleared space and begin sawing down the back of the adjacent stone. Meanwhile, another sawyer would be employed making further vertical cuts down the face. Once the sawing was complete and blocks were free on both sides, back and top, they could be easily wedged from the bed and removed by crane. After the top bed was taken out it was a relatively easy task to saw the back of the beds below and remove the stone in the same manner. A quarryman

Above: This photograph, taken at Hartham Park quarry, shows two quarrymen cutting the lower beds of stone with large stone saws known as 'frig bobs'. Meanwhile another worker is preparing to make a back cut, separating the block of stone from the face. The fourth quarryman appears to be lubricating the saws with water to wash away stone debris.

Below: A hand operated wooden crane used to lift a cut block of stone from the lower bed.

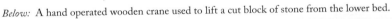

Above: illustrating the conservative nature of the Corsham stone industry, this photo, taken in 1948, shows quarryman Bill Stevens leading a horse-drawn stone truck on an underground haulageway in Park Lane quarry.

Left: Horses were stabled below ground during the week at Park Lane quarry, and brought to the surface at weekends. Note the large stack of cut ashlar blocks in the background of this image.

Above: Box quarrymen pose for the photographer outside Clift quarry in 1896

Below: A similar photograph, taken ten years earlier in 1886. Note the oil lamps attached to small wooden boards carried by the men in the back row. These would be supported by slots cut in the working face to provide illumination underground.

Above: The workshop staff at Clift Quarry, towards the end of the nineteenth century.

Below: Banker masons at Box Tan Yard shortly before the First World War.

Bath Stone Firms' quarrymen and
masons pose beneath a large stacking
crane at Spring Quarry stacking yard
in 1886

would saw vertically at the rate of approximately one foot per hour and to prevent the saw blade jamming in the groove during this process it was usual to place a can full of water, with a small hole near the bottom, adjacent to the cut. A matchstick inserted into the hole would direct a small flow of water into the cut, thus lubricating the saw and washing out debris on each back stroke.

Once cut from the working face the blocks, which were usually between 50 and 150 cubic feet and might weigh anything up to about five tons each, were roughly squared-up, loaded by crane on to low, horse-drawn wagons or narrow-gauge railway trucks, (frequently horse-drawn, but in the latter phases of the industry propelled by steam or diesel locomotives), and transported to a stacking area. Normally, during the summer months cut stone would be taken directly to a surface stacking yard, but in winter the usual practice was to store the stone underground for several months to allow it to lose much of its moisture content. If taken to the surface in winter there was a risk that the high moisture content in the blocks might freeze and cause them to disintegrate in the frost. When the industry was at its peak in the early years of the twentieth century the Corsham area was producing many thousands of tons of stone annually and, to transship this huge volume, a complex network of interlinked tramways had developed, connecting all the Bath & Portland Stone Firm's quarries to loading platforms at the mainline railway stations at Box and Corsham. In addition, there were extensive stacking yards at each of the quarries together with a vast central storage yard established in the fields south of Corsham station. An independent narrow-gauge railway system connected the quarries at Monkton Farleigh with a rail transfer at Farleigh Down Sidings, to the west of Box, and with a roadside wharf on Bathford High Street.

Many of the more remote quarries in the Avon valley were, as we have already seen, also connected to the railway or canal by means of inclined tramways. Part of the stone produced was shipped out as large, rough-squared block, but much was worked locally, either cut into ashlar or worked to customer requirements in the many masons yards, large and small, that proliferated in close proximity to the railway in both Box and Corsham. When one looks at the photographs on the pages that follow it is easy to fall into the trap of assuming that the quarrymen laboured in a brightly illuminated workspace, but nothing could be further from the truth. The photographs, for the most part, were taken using multiple flash exposures from a single electronic flash gun, and often took up to an hour each to complete. Up until about 1870 the only source of light underground was provided by inefficient and very smoky tallow candles. These were expensive commodities which were not provided by the quarrymasters but which the quarrymen had to purchase themselves. Consequently only the very minimum tended to be used and hence the men generally worked in an atmosphere of constant, pervasive gloom. By the mid-1870s small oil lamps were becoming

Above: the entrance to Clift Quarry, adjacent to the stone works on Box Hill, in the mid-1930s. Note the gantry crane and the tramway tracks, used initially by horse drawn trucks but latterly by a small diesel locomotive.

Left: Clift works yard, near the quarry entrance, with a large block of freshly cut stone being unloaded from a narrow-gauge truck.

widespread in the quarries but these too were expensive and many quarrymen made their own, fabricated from old tins. Shortly after the First World War acetylene lamps became commonplace. These lamps, fueled by calcium carbide and water, were much more efficient and gave a controllable, intense white light. Mounds of spent carbide, often several feet deep, are widespread throughout the quarries that remained in operation beyond the First World War.

SECTION 2

QUARRY TRAMWAYS

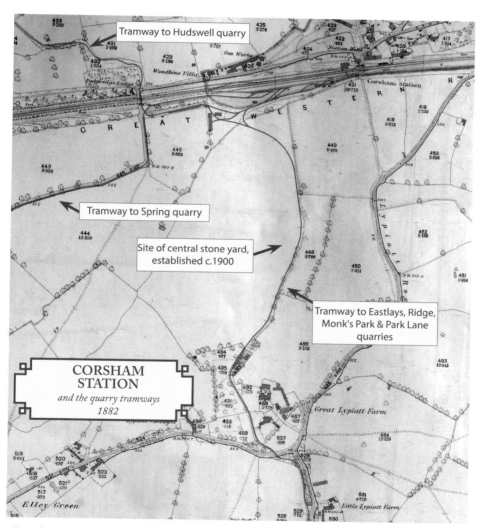

Tramway to Hudswell quarry

Tramway to Spring quarry

Site of central stone yard, established c.1900

Tramway to Eastlays, Ridge, Monk's Park & Park Lane quarries

CORSHAM STATION

and the quarry tramways
1882

Above: As was touched upon in the introduction, following the amalgamation of almost all the Corsham quarries under the ownership of the Bath Stone Firms, a complex system of interlinked tramways developed linking the majority of those quarries to a central stone stacking yard and to main line railway loading facilities at Corsham and Box stations. This plan shows the tramway layout serving Corsham station and the central stone yard.

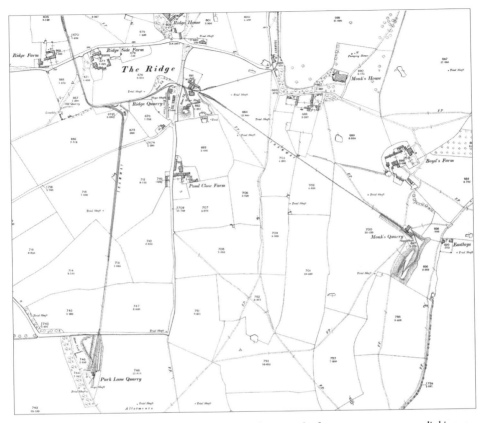

Above: This 1902 Ordnance Survey plan shows the complex network of narrow-gauge tramways linking Park Lane, Ridge and Eastlays (shown here as Monks Quarry) to the central stacking yard and thence to the railway loading platforms at Corsham station. Note the two road crossings near Ridge Side Farm and a little to the east by the duck pond. Although the rails are long-gone, the routes of many of the tramways are still discernible as wide, straight hedgerows or as slightly raised causeways or embankments across the fields.

Note too the large number of 'trial shafts' marked on the map; these were sunk to the assumed level of the oolitic limestone stratum to determine the extent of the stone reserves in the area. Frequently, if the tests were positive, the trial shafts would become integrated into the quarries as ventilation shafts.

Right: This plan shows the quarries and quarry tramways to the west of the area seen on the plan above. Most prominent is the very large stacking yard at Spring Quarry, in the centre of the image. Several of the smaller quarries, including Seven Shaft, Sands, and Moor Park quarry (shown at the bottom right of the plan), have small internal tramways but are not linked to the main Bath Stone Firms system. Huddswell Quarry (top right) is unusual that it is accessed directly by a standard-gauge branch from the GWR main line via a subsidiary tunnel adjacent to the east portal of Box Tunnel, and also by steam-powered lifts in vertical shafts.

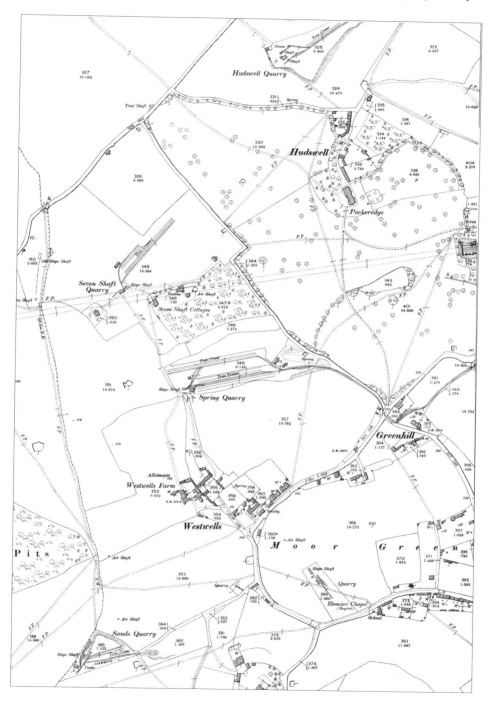

27

Above: A loaded stone wagon on the passing loop at the bottom of Spring Quarry stacking yard. The man in the foreground is Tom Butler and the young man behind is Jack Cainey.

Below: This view of the yard at Spring Quarry, taken just prior to the First World War, gives some idea of the prodigious quantities of stone produced when the industry was at its peak.

Above: Taken at Park Lane quarry in 1912, this image shows a pair of horses being prepared to haul a block of stone from the quarry to the loading bank at Corsham station. The building on the left houses the haulage engine used to draw wagons up the inclined shaft.

Below: A rake of laden stone trucks from Park Lane quarry waits in the passing loop near Ridge quarry before continuing on its journey to Corsham station yard.

Above: Monks Park's two-foot gauge Muir Hill locomotive transferring a couple of heavily loaded stone trucks in the yard in the late 1950s.

Below: A decade later, the Muir Hill engine at Monks Park appears to have been replaced by this somewhat beefier looking, unidentified diesel-powered mining engine.

Above: Rail mounted stacking crane in the yard at Eastlays Quarry, probably late 19th Century.

Below: An early view of the east end of Box Tunnel, showing the Hockney & Hartham Park Stone Company's standard gauge branch line entering Tunnel quarry via a portal to north of the GWR main line tunnel.

SECTION 3

THE QUARRIES TODAY

As we saw in the introduction to this book, the surviving evidence of the stone quarrying industry in the Corsham area, as far as the actual extraction of stone for building purposes is concerned, can be seen to represent four distinct phases:

- The huge areas of long-worked-out quarry where all the stone was extracted probably by the end of the nineteenth century.
- The areas of quarry still worked in the 1930s but abandoned when requisitioned for government purposes and now largely, but not entirely, 'preserved-in-aspic' behind the security barrier of the quarries still occupied since the Second World War by the Ministry of Defence.
- The small number of quarries that recommenced working after the war and limped on until the 1960s or a little later.
- The even smaller number of quarries where work has resumed in the last forty years or so, using relatively modern methods and machinery.

WARTIME REQUISITIONS

Between 1934 and 1940, all the quarries in the Corsham area were acquired by purchase or compulsory requisition by the government for various wartime purposes. Much of the underground real estate remains in government hands; some are retained but disused, others still play important military roles. Following the pre-war and wartime requisition, surveys of the quarries made by the military engineers indicated that there were large area that were unsuitable for conversion and these were simply abandoned, often sequestered behind the boundary walls of the government bunkers. Thus inaccessible by the general public, these areas have remained exactly as they were some eighty years ago, often with the quarrymen's tools still left in place, in the erroneous hope that they would return to work as soon as hostilities ended. What is especially interesting to the industrial archaeologist is that, because the Bath & Portland Stone Company was so conservative in its outlook, the tools and methods used in the 1930s were little different than those used in the 1830s, so those areas more-or-less accidentally preserved by government custody present a remarkably accurate image of the quarrying industry of almost two centuries ago, as some of the following photographs will show.

Above: Probably the most iconic view in the whole Corsham underground complex; this is the Cathedral, an early, vertical shaft quarry worked by Job Pictor between 1829 and 1850. Whereas at other vertical shaft quarries in the Corsham and Monkton Farleigh areas (for example Huddswell quarry in Corsham and Norbin Barton quarry near South Wraxhall), the vertical shafts were sunk to the stone stratum and then worked out horizontally, *all* the stone in the Cathedral was excavated as the shaft descended, resulting in this huge bell-shaped chamber some 190 feet long and 100 feet in depth.

Above & below: Examples of Victorian quarrymen's graffiti that can be found throughout the quarries. Some reflect current affairs, some are humorous and some are humorously obscene. In the image below the text near the representation of a donkey reads 'Farmer Sheppard, Donkey Captain' while the image to the left is annotated 'Box Rifle Volunteers'.

Above: This depiction of an early steam locomotive may be a naive representation of Brunel's 'Thunderer' of 1839, or more likely Gooch's 'Thunderer', which ran on the main line through Box Tunnel for more than twenty years, after its first appearance in 1851. The wheel arrangement, however, is incorrect for either locomotive.

Below: This is probably a composite depiction of a locomotive hauling a train of stone wagons out of the quarry tunnel mouth adjacent to the main line tunnel at Box. Notice what appears to be a brakesman with his brake-stick on the rear of the engine.

Above: closed and sealed off during the construction of the War Office ammunition storage depot at Tunnel Quarry in the mid-1930s, this is the slope shaft that once gave access to Seven Shaft quarry. The iron grill at the top of the shaft was a War Office installation allowing the flow of ventilation but preventing physical access. The shaft and steps are coated in a thick deposit of calcite, the result of some ninety years flow of seepage water.

Below: The inclined shaft access to Sands quarry, a relatively small working adjacent to the south-west extremity of Spring quarry. During the post-war development of Spring Quarry by the MoD, Sands quarry was adapted as an emergency exit from the Spring quarry complex.

Above: The Bath & Portland Stone Company continued to work parts of Spring Quarry right up until 1940, when, overnight, it was requisitioned by the government. Parts of the quarry, however, were found to be unsuitable for conversion into factory space, and these abandoned areas have remained walled-up, both literally behind brick and concrete barriers and metaphorically behind curtains of military security, for eighty years. What remains, like these wooden cranes, is living archaeology, preserved for posterity.

Above & below: Here in Spring Quarry we see cranes and crowbars, stone saws and other tools, along with personal possessions like boots and beer-bottles, left by the quarrymen who, on 7th December 1940, were ordered not to return to work the following day.

Above: A superb view of a working face in Spring Quarry with, propped against the left-hand wall, a set of scissor-shaped shears for lifting stone blocks with the crane. The decidedly ancient looking writing on the right-hand wall, dated 1852, is something of a mystery as this section of the quarry was not worked until the 1930s....

Below: A crane positioned next to the tramway, ready to load blocks directly onto wagons.

Brewer's Yard quarry, in the woodland at Rudloe Firs near the top of Box Hill, is unusual that it was worked on two distinct levels. Both were accessed via a vertical shaft, while a slope shaft gave additional access to the upper level. A flight of steps, seen here, led down to the lower level.

Above: Considerable quantities of cut ashlar blocks remain in the lower level of Brewer's Yard quarry, probably abandoned when the quarry was requisition for government use in November 1940. It would appear that Brewer's Yard was considered as an extension to the Copenacre Admiralty storage facility, but this plan was not proceeded with.

Below: The well-built wall on the left of this image of Brewer's Yard was constructed merely to hold back heaps of waste stone or *gob*, generated during the quarrying process.

Above: Bradley Wyatt perches precariously on the edge of the upper level of the vertical shaft at Brewer's Yard quarry. The shaft extends upwards by about seventy feet to the surface and descends a further fifty feet or so to the lower level of the quarry. The shaft was the means by which cut stone was removed from the quarry; the quarrymen gained access via an extraordinarily steep inclined shaft.

Below: This panoramic image shows the whole extent of Hollybush quarry in Neston, a somewhat unsuccessful venture which only lasted for a short time, closing in December 1902.
The rubble-filled slope-shaft entrance is to the right of the photo and the ventilation shaft is near the end of the main passage, seen on the left.

Above: Geoff Holstead poses beside the bottom of the ventilation shaft at Hollybush quarry. Originally this was a trial shaft sunk to prove the extent of the stone reserves. The slope shaft was sunk a few hundred yards to the north and the main underground heading then proceeded towards the original shaft.

Above: The bottom of the original slope shaft to Park Lane quarry. This quarry was worked for a few years after the Second World War but was prone to flooding and the entrance sealed. Quarrying resumed here in recent years using a completely new shaft nearer the best remaining stone, and to meet local authority planning requirements.

Below: the wide areas of unsupported roof, seen here in a typical area of Park Lane quarry, bear witness to the quality of stone extracted and to the remarkable stability of the quarry.

Above: Near the bottom of the inclined shaft at Park Lane quarry is a stable, seen on the left of this view, where the horses used for underground haulage were kept during week-days. The soot marks on the ceiling are from the diesel locomotive that displaced the horses post-war.

Below: An interior view of the stables; note the neatly cobbled floor.

POST-WAR REOPENING

By December 1940 all the quarries in the Corsham area had been requisitioned by the government and put into the care of the Ministry of Works, which undertook surveys, found suitable uses for them on behalf of various military departments and industrial concerns and, in the initial phases, arranged contracts for their conversion for their wartime functions. Initially there was no overall plan, but the blanket requisition ensured that the government had immediate access to the maximum possible amount of secure, underground real estate. By 1946 it was apparent that several of the quarries which had never found a wartime function were surplus to the government's requirement and were handed back to their previous owners, principally the Bath & Portland Stone Company.

Bath & Portland had learned some lessons from the wartime years which they proceeded to exploit post-war. During the late 1930s when the Central Ammunition Depot was under construction, many thousands of unemployed colliery workers from North East England and South Wales were drafted in to undertake the conversion work, and they brought with them all the expertise in the use of modern mining equipment which the Bath & Portland Company had largely ignored as a result of the cheap labour that had always been available to them. With construction completed and the war over, much of this plant – including electrically powered 'Samson' and 'Dreadnought' coal cutters, Siskol and Hardiax arc-shearers and diesel and electric traction rather than traditional horse-power – became redundant and was purchased by Bath & Portland and used with varying degrees of success.

Below: A Hardiax pneumatic arc-shearer, a legacy of the wartime occupation, in use at Monk's Park quarry to cut a picking bed.

Right: A modern steel development of the Victorian wooden stone crane at work in Monk's Park Quarry.

Below: A Greenbat battery electric mining locomotive in service in Monk's Park quarry. The stacking crane appears to be an ancient and modern hybrid design....

Above: An electrically powered 'Samson' coal cutter at work in Monk's Park. Although cuts in all directions could be made very quickly with these machines, they had two disadvantages: firstly they produced copious amounts of dust, and secondly, because of the great width of the cutting chain a fair amount of good stone was lost.

Below: A 'Dreadnought' coal cutter being prepared to make a vertical cut in Monk's Park quarry in the early 1980s. The chap to the left of the machine is Derek Hawkins who provided many of the photographs used in this book.

Above: Loading a block onto a wagon in Monk's Park, using the quarry's electric stacking crane.

Below: A bucket loader used to clear waste stone in Monks Park quarry, around 2001.

Above: Monk's Park's Greenwood & Batley electric locomotive, with a couple of modern steel-bodied trucks in the background.

Below: A small Ruston Hornsby 0-4-0 diesel locomotive at Monk's Park.

Above: The underground stacking ground at Monk's Park. This high-roofed area formerly housed a concrete making plant, providing material for construction of the adjacent Admiralty underground store.

Below: The all-steel crane fixed at a working face in Monk's Park, with a 'Samson' machine in the background. Notice the vertical drill marks in the stone below the crane; this is evidence of another method of cutting blocks using a drill and then 'plugs & feathers' to break away the stone.

Above: Monk's Park: a large block of stone weighing probably five tons, chained to trolley ready to be drawn to the surface.

Below: The winch room at Monk's Park. In the background can be seen a large block on a trolley coming over the brow of the incline. A shed next to the winch room once housed a wartime searchlight generator, intended as a standby power source for the winch in event of a mains failure.

A loaded stone trolley emerging from the inclined shaft at Monk's Park. This image indicates the steep gradient of the shaft.
The rusty metalwork to the right of the shaft top consists of several derelict Samson coal cutters, which were constantly cannibalised for spare parts.

Left: The main passage into Clift quarry, from the entrance on Box Hill. Originally, narrow gauge rails were laid in this passage, and the soot marks on the ceiling were made by the locomotive, which superceded horse-haulage, used to haul stone from the working faces out to the cutting yard.

Below: The other side of the stone arch seen in the photograph to the left. The rectangular stone structure to the left of the passageway is a large water tank, used to provide water for the quarrymen's acetylene lamps. The pile of debris around the foot of the tank is spent calcium carbide that was used to fuel the lamps.

Above: The last heading worked by the Bath & Portland Stone Company prior to the closure of Clift quarry in 1968. Note the drill marks, indicating that stone in this area was removed by drilling a series of holes with a pneumatic drill along the cut line and then finishing the job by sawing through the line of holes with a frig-bob.

Below: One of several abandoned stone cranes in Clift quarry.

Above: A typical scene in Clift quarry. In the lead-up to the Second World War, Clift quarry was used as a through-route for men and materials involved in the construction of Tunnel Quarry ammunition depot. The wooden props seen here are not typical of local stone quarrying practice, but were widely used by the colliers drafted in on the government works programme.

Right: Cut stone blocks in Clift quarry, trapped by a roof fall.

Above: Immediately after the government released some of the quarries back to the Bath & Portland Stone Company, the company began experimenting with the Samson coal cutters previously used on the War Office works. Here we see a Samson machine cutting into the lower bed of stone in Moor Park quarry. In the background can be seen a face where blocks have been successfully cut by machine, although, due to the limited clearance, the back-cuts have had to be drilled.

Left: Here the swivelling head of the Samson has been turned to the horizontal position to make a top-cut.

Above: In later years production ceased underground at Moor Park although the surface cutting yard remained active. Stone slurry from the processing plant was pumped underground and gradually filled most of the workings to a depth of several feet.

Above: As the author discovered while photographing the workings, one had to move quickly to avoid sinking waist-deep in the slurry.....

The locomotive shed in Moor Park quarry, disused but with the track still in place. Following closure of the quarry and the surface cutting yard, the Moor Park housing estate has been built on the site.

Above: 21st Century quarrying at Hartham Park quarry: a remotely controlled, electro-hydraulic cutting machine at work.

Below: A typical roadway in Hartham Park quarry. Note the roof bolts used to secure the roof.

SECTION 4

WARTIME

As we have seen, by the summer of 1934 the British government and the military strategists upon whom it relied were convinced that another major European war was inevitable.

Over the ensuing six months virtually every cave, quarry and abandoned mine in Britain was examined and reported upon. The sites visited included salt mines in Cheshire, limestone and gypsum quarries in Derbyshire and Cumberland, slate quarries in North Wales, disused railway tunnels throughout the whole of Britain and, most significantly, oolitic limestone quarries in north Wiltshire. Most were immediately dismissed as unsuitable due to dampness, geological instability, remoteness from transport links or the difficulty of obtaining sufficient labour locally to undertake the task of conversion. Twenty or so sites were singled out for further attention but none, except for the Wiltshire stone quarries, appeared particularly promising.

Attention soon focused upon the vast subterranean network of stone quarries in the vicinity of Corsham in Wiltshire which, as we have seen, were run more-or-less as a monopoly by the Bath & Portland Stone Company. At the time of the Royal Engineers' visit the Bath & Portland company was running into financial difficulties. Although there was still stone left in its quarries the reserves were running out and that which was left was generally of slightly lower quality and was more difficult to extract. With Britain entering the worst recession the economy had ever experienced the building industry was in decline and consequently the market for building stone was quickly contracting. The company, as we have seen, faced other problems too. Stone quarrying in Wiltshire was a highly conservative and labour intensive industry. Historically, there was always a surplus of labour so wages were low and there was no incentive to mechanize. The most startling feature of the underground quarries in the early 1930s was that the tools and techniques being used to extract stone were the same tools and techniques that were being used when Queen Victoria ascended to the throne. By the middle of the decade, however, things were changing. Wage rates generally were rising and, with the government's belated re-armament programme stimulating manufacturing industries, there was suddenly more competition for labour. All of these factors threatened the viability of the Bath & Portland Stone Company which found itself saddled with rapidly increasing labour costs, falling demand and the dead-weight overhead costs of a dozen or more unproductive quarries. Thus, when the directors were approached by the War Office with tentative enquiries about the prospective purchase of some of their freehold quarries at commercial rates they were overjoyed.

Within the War Office there were men who were already aware of the potential value of the Corsham quarries, for under their aegis during the First World War, Ridge Quarry, a small underground working approximately six acres in extent situated near the village of Neston, had been temporarily occupied on behalf of the Ministry of Munitions for the storage of high-explosives for which no suitable accommodation could be found at Woolwich Arsenal. In January 1935 the War Office was given permission to make surveys of all the Bath & Portland quarries in the Corsham area and, based upon the result of these surveys, Ridge Quarry and the much larger, fifty-acre Tunnel Quarry just to the north of Brunel's Box railway tunnel, were purchased on 15 August for the sum of £35,000. A few months later Eastlays Quarry at Gastard was acquired, followed by Monkton Farleigh Quarry in March 1937. These four quarries jointly encompassed an area of approximately 150 acres and were later to become 'Central Ammunition Depot Corsham'.

A year or so after the War Office initiated its quest for underground accommodation the Air Ministry began a similar search. In 1934 the RAF was essentially a force of wooden biplane fighters and light, short-range bombers designed principally for army support duties. It was not until the series of expansion programmes, with their emphasis on fast, metal-skinned monoplane fighters and heavy bombers, got under way in 1930s that the Air Ministry realized that it had no secure storage sites for the munitions that would arm its new range of aircraft. By the summer of 1936 bombs in huge quantities were rolling out of British factories, swelling the tide of similar weapons imported from the United States that were trundling on trains from the ports en route to the RAF's only, and hopelessly inefficient, armament storage depot at Altrincham in Cheshire, which had been designed solely for the maintenance of small-arms ammunition. At this point the Air Ministry Works Department, entrusted with the task of locating underground storage capacity for its burgeoning stockpile of bombs, was disconcerted to find that all the best sites had already been snapped up by the War Office. As an interim emergency measure the War Office was persuaded in 1936 to hand over the majority of Ridge Quarry, then nearing completion, to the RAF and in the following year permission was also obtained to occupy part of the Eastlays depot at Corsham.

Meanwhile the search for their own dedicated underground capacity continued. Eventually five sites were secured, none of which were ideal and three of which proved to be catastrophic failures. Initially three old mine workings were identified: Chilmark Quarry near Wilton in Wiltshire that had provided stone for the construction of Salisbury Cathedral, Linley Caverns near Brownhill in Staffordshire that a century earlier had provided building stone for Birmingham but which, since late Victorian times, had intermittently functioned as a tourist attraction, and the Fauld gypsum mine near Burton-on-Trent in Staffordshire. The Chilmark depot was the least unsuccessful of the Air Ministry ventures underground. Despite the fact that it was subject to frequent and unexpected roof falls throughout its life it survived the Second World War intact and remained in RAF service until the early 1990s. Linley caverns proved disastrous; intermittent flooding of the lower levels and frequent roof falls in the upper galleries led to its abandonment even before construction was complete. Fauld mine was developed into an enormous, fifty-acre underground storage depot rivaling in scale the immense army depots beneath Corsham. The mine at Fauld became the principal RAF storage depot and home to the RAF's Master Provisioning Officer and staff who were responsible for the overall logistics of keeping airfields throughout Britain supplied with weapons. It functioned efficiently and without incident until 27 November 1944 when careless handling of a high-explosive bomb resulted in the simultaneous detonation of some 4,000 tons of high-explosives deep underground. The explosion was the largest non-nuclear detonation the world has ever seen. Castle Hayes Farm, situated directly above the seat of the blast, evaporated, other adjacent farms were almost completely destroyed and there was widespread damage in surrounding towns and villages. A dam supplying water to a nearby plasterboard works was breached resulting in the flooding of the factory by a deluge of mud and the loss of dozens of lives. The resultant crater, one hundred feet deep and almost a quarter of a mile in diameter, remains as a monument to those who died in the blast and is clearly visible in satellite imagery today.

Long before the occurrences of the disasters that dogged their subterranean adventures the Air Ministry, finding themselves beaten by the War Office in the race to acquire suitable abandoned underground real estate, decided to take a different approach and build instead their own 'artificial' underground bomb stores. In the summer of 1938 an extensive open quarry at Harpur Hill near Buxton was purchased from Imperial Chemical Industries Ltd. The former limestone quarry – worked to provide not building stone or aggregate but raw material for a number of chemical processes – was almost one hundred feet deep and had good rail access. A single-storey reinforced concrete structure consisting of a series of parallel arched tunnels, with their walls pierced at regular intervals to allow free access across the width of the depot, was built in the bottom of the quarry and when completed was overlain with forty feet of loose rock debris to give additional protection against aerial bombardment. Due to the sloping nature of the quarry floor it was found that a lower, second level could be incorporated into the design of the bomb store for part of its length. When the depot became operational this lower area was used to store chemical weapons.

Just a month before the outbreak of war a slate quarry at Llanberis in North Wales, similar in dimension to the limestone quarry at Harpur Hill, was acquired and developed in a similar manner, except that the extraordinary depth of the quarry at Llanberis allowed a double-level underground structure to be built. At both locations tunnels into the hillside enabled standard-gauge ammunition trains to enter deep into the depots in order to transship their cargoes at secure underground loading platforms.

Unfortunately, due to a combination of faulty design, poor quality materials and inexperienced labour, both depots were fatally flawed. On 25 January 1942, only six months after coming into service, two thirds of the Llanberis depot collapsed within seconds under the weight of the overlying backfill, burying a train that was unloading at the time and trapping 14,000 tons of high-explosive bombs. An examination of the Harpur Hill site revealed disturbingly ominous cracks developing in the structure there also, so an emergency evacuation of all stocks was ordered. Many of the bombs previously stored in or destined for the Harpur Hill and Llanberis depots were diverted to Corsham where additional space was set aside in the War Office reserve depots. Although this was ostensibly a temporary arrangement the RAF remained in occupation of much of the Eastlays site at Corsham throughout the war. Meanwhile, recovery work at Llanberis continued for more than a year before the final buried bomb was rescued and the debris cleared from the site. The surviving sections of the tunnels at Llanberis were reinforced and much remedial work undertaken at Harpur Hill but the Air Ministry had lost confidence in the structural stability of both depots. The tunnels at Llanberis were never re-occupied and Harpur Hill was subsequently used to store only unfilled bomb casings and obsolete weapons pending disposal.

While the Army and Air Force were scrambling to acquire the seemingly sparse amount of underground space available on commercial terms, the Admiralty remained obstinately aloof. With some justification they argued that the weight and physical size of most naval ammunition was such that handling it underground, and particularly retrieval via inclined access shafts like those at the army ammunition depots at Corsham, would render such a storage solution unfeasible. Their preference was to retain the limited surface storage capacity they already had with additional accommodation for the excess in floating hulks, supplemented by a huge number of railway wagons parked indefinitely in railway sidings in close proximity to the naval dockyards. In 1938 the Admiralty stance underwent a rapid reversal and the concept of underground storage was suddenly embraced with great enthusiasm. Plans were prepared for two massively-engineered and monumentally expensive tunneled storage facilities at Dean Hill, south of Salisbury in Wiltshire and at Trecwn in west Wales. To overcome the difficulties previously identified with underground storage

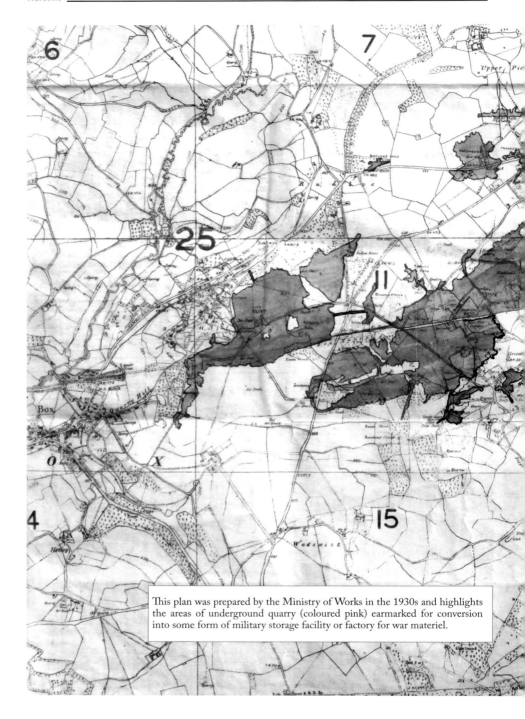

This plan was prepared by the Ministry of Works in the 1930s and highlights the areas of underground quarry (coloured pink) earmarked for conversion into some form of military storage facility or factory for war materiel.

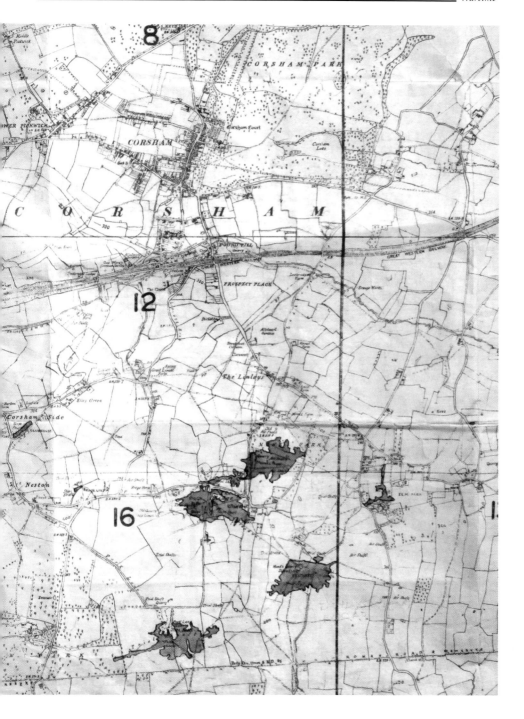

the two new Admiralty depots were designed as a series of short, horizontal concrete-lined tunnels bored herringbone-fashion into hillsides. At Dean Hill the tunnels were in two closely spaced groups along a chalk hillside while at Trecwn the two groups were burrowed into opposite sides of a narrow valley. A complex network of narrow-gauge railways connected the individual storage tunnels to standard-gauge interchange sidings.

With war now looming inevitably on the near horizon, and with reserve stocks of ammunition increasing at an alarming rate, the Admiralty reluctantly decided in October 1938, at the time of the Munich crisis, that they would have to adopt some sort of existing underground storage, at least as a temporary measure until Trecwn and Dean Hill were completed and commissioned, in order to release some of the railway wagons that were seriously congesting the sidings at Portsmouth and elsewhere. By that time, however, there was little available and they were compelled to take up a number of small, inconvenient and in many ways unsuitable quarries; one at Beer in south Devon and three – Brockleaze, Traveler's Rest and Elm Park quarries – at Corsham. Custody of the latter quarry was a matter of some contention between the Air Ministry, who claimed to have discovered it first with a view to using it as a lubricating oil store, and the Admiralty who eventually found themselves in grudgingly disputed possession.

THE FALL OF FRANCE

An important feature of the series of underground acquisitions made by various government departments during the 1930s is that they were all undertaken in peacetime and under conventional commercial terms. When Monkton Farleigh Quarry, the last of the Corsham quarries, was purchased by the War Office in 1937 and land acquired for the Admiralty's Trecwn complex in 1938, it appeared at the time that Britain's subterranean military adventures were complete.

Similarly, the plans of another highly secretive and very important government organization, the Museums and Galleries Air Raids Precautions Committee, appeared to have been put into operation smoothly. Its task was to evacuate all the pictures and other artifacts in the London museums and galleries to places of safety for the duration of the war. To this end the committee had entered into secret negotiations with the owners of remote country houses throughout the 'safe' area of the country who were willing, as a patriotic endeavor, to take custody of the treasures until the conflict was over. A list of forty properties, known as the National Register, was drawn up early in 1935 and each was allocated a particular museum or gallery from which it would receive at least a proportion of the contents. Artifacts from the Victoria & Albert Museum, for example, were allocated to Montacute House in Somerset, pictures from the

National Gallery to Penrhyn Castle and other properties in North Wales, the contents of the British Museum to Boughton House in Northamptonshire and Skipton Castle in Yorkshire, pictures from the Tate Gallery to 'Old Quarries' at Avening in Gloucestershire, to 'Hellens' at Much Marcle and to Eastington Hall nearby. Preparations were made for the evacuation years in advance; a special LMS train, for example, was kept constantly in steam at Camden goods yard from the summer of 1935, waiting for the day that it would be called upon to whisk the contents of the National Gallery northwards to Penrhyn beyond the shield of the Snowdon mountains.

When the evacuation happened, just hours before the declaration of war, all went smoothly and within just a few days every picture and artifact reached its allocated destination safely. Nothing was lost and nothing damaged. For a few months the scheme had all the appearances of success, but in the early spring of 1940 it all broke down in chaos. The owners of the country houses, already hard pressed by rising taxation and falling rents, discovered that the Treasury expected them to foot the bills for the extra fuel required to maintain reasonable environmental conditions for the artifacts in their care, to finance the structural alterations and repairs required and to pay for the necessary security measures. Most of the larger institutions wished to maintain their peacetime procedures during the period of evacuation. The business of new acquisitions, restoration and cataloguing would go on more or less as normal, but to accomplish this it was necessary that key members of staff should be evacuated along with the pictures and pots. To their horror, the property owners found that the museum and gallery trustees expected these staff members to be treated as country house guests – as if on a weekend retreat – that free accommodation should be provided for them and that the family servants should wait upon them.

Tensions at the country houses was reaching the point of rebellion in the early Spring of 1940, but the tipping-point came with the Fall of France in June. Previously, as we have seen, German bombers flying from homeland airfields could reach only the tip of England but now, in possession of French airfields all along the channel coast, the Luftwaffe could range over the whole of Britain. Skies over the previously safe areas west and north of the Wash-Solent line were opened to the enemy and all the previously secure provincial country houses vulnerable to attack. The Treasury, which was in overall control of the museum evacuation plan, realized that swift and unpalatable action was required. From the inception of the scheme in 1934 the Treasury had been opposed to underground storage for the art treasures and antiquities on both financial and political grounds. Financially, they were aware that the limited funding available for war preparations was better spent upon material required for the armed services; politically, there was a feeling that it would be dangerous, in the words of a government official, to "*spend money protecting elitist trifles when we have announced that there will be no provision of deep level air raid shelters for the population of London."* There was now little option but to go underground and a frantic search began for suitable accommodation. The problem was that other government departments, too, were now seeking subterranean capacity on an unprecedented scale. Chief amongst these was the Ministry of Aircraft Production, under the abrasive leadership of Lord Beaverbrook, with ambitions to transfer the entire British aircraft industry into an immense network of underground factories.

Eventually two more or less suitable locations were found. Following painstaking investigation and negotiation by Brigadier H. Temple-Richards, the senior civil engineer at the Ministry of Works Defence Architect's Department, an enormous and terribly wet underground slate quarry was discovered at Manod in the Snowdon mountains. This was subsequently adapted with much ingenuity to house the 2,000 pictures from the National Gallery that had previously sheltered at Penrhyn Castle and elsewhere in North Wales.

Meanwhile, in Wiltshire, parts of Westwood Quarry near Bradford-on-Avon was acquired by the Museums and Galleries Air Raids Precautions Committee and, by the summer of 1942, had been converted into a vast underground repository to house all the treasures from the British Museum, the Victoria & Albert Museum, the National Portrait Gallery, Science Museum, Imperial War Museum, British and Bodleian libraries and some forty other of London's museums, galleries and archives all of which had, earlier in the war, been distributed widely under the country house scheme.

THE UNDERGROUND FACTORIES

The threat to Britain's art treasures in the wake of the French capitulation was as nothing compared to that which faced Britain's survival as a nation. All of the RAF's defensive airfields in southern England were now open to German aerial bombardment and it was expected that the full weight of the Luftwaffe would be hurled against them. Once the RAF's airfields and its fighter force were destroyed Germany would be in command of British airspace and the war would be lost.

The viability of Fighter Command as a defensive force depended upon three elements: pilots, aircraft and airfields. Experience had shown that the Air Ministry Works Department was remarkably adept at getting airfields up and running after they had sustained even serious bomb damage, but the loss of pilots and aircraft were more intractable problems. Replacement pilots took some time to train but there was a constant stream of young men going through the process and, anyway, the loss of an aeroplane did not always also mean the loss of a pilot. Lost aircraft, however, required a skilled workforce, scarce and valuable material resources and a finite amount of time to replace, and needed extensive and immobile premises in which to manufacture them. It was assumed that the Luftwaffe attacks would be targeted against both the airfields and the aeroplane factories, for if the factories were destroyed then the RAF would be unable to replace the aircraft that were destroyed.

Immediate steps were taken to safeguard the aircraft manufacturing facilities. During the height of the Battle of Britain measures were already being taken to disperse elements of the most important aircraft factories from the industrial cities to remote country locations. Fears that Germany would turn her attacks from the airfields, where stiff opposition had been felt, to London and the industrial cities were justified by the commencement of the London blitz in September 1940. The vulnerability of the aircraft industry was highlighted when the Bristol Aeroplane Company's engine plant at Filton near Bristol was attacked on the nights of 25th and 27th September and 160 workers killed.

Clearly, an enhanced programme of dispersal was an urgent necessity but the Minister of Aircraft Production, Lord Beaverbrook, thought this inadequate and in October 1940 issued an edict to the effect that within six months underground accommodation would have to be found for the entire British aircraft industry. The response from the Treasury and the Ministry of Works was not encouraging. Beaverbrook was told that there was insufficient existing underground space capable of adaptation to house more than a tiny fraction of the surface factory accommodation, that there was no money to finance the construction of new, purpose-built tunnels and that, even if there was sufficient money and sufficient resources and labour, the excavation alone would take three years to complete. Over the following month Beaverbrook's plan was rolled back to the point where, towards the end of November, it was decided that only the aircraft engine factories should be transferred underground. Further rationalization, at the insistence of the Treasury, resulted in the scheme being restricted only to the Filton engine plant of the Bristol Aeroplane Company.

Once again the search was concentrated in the Corsham area. Four quarries were identified as suitable although all four were still being actively worked by the Bath & Portland company, though on a very limited scale. The four locations were Spring Quarry, a huge and rambling labyrinth of tunnels extending over 3,300,000 square feet, Westwood Quarry (of which we have earlier heard mention) some 250,000 square feet in extent, and two smaller quarries at Limpley Stoke and Monks Park. The process of acquisition was in sharp contrast to that employed by the War Office in the mid- 1930s. On 5 December 1940 the regional requisitioning officer made a peremptory call upon the offices of the Bath & Portland Stone Company with a requisition order for all four quarries which were to be transferred to government control that day. Labourers working in the quarries were laid-off with one day's notice and told not to return to work the following day.

It was intended that all four quarries should be handed over to the Bristol Aeroplane Company; Spring, Westwood and Monks Park quarries would be used for production while Limpley Stoke would become a warehouse to house a buffer stock of completed engines in excess of those for immediate consumption by the airframe manufacturers. Unfortunately the scheme began to unravel after the first day. Custody of Monks Park quarry was contested by the Admiralty who claimed to have made a prior request for its requisition, the argument continuing for several months with inconclusive result. At one point a third party, the Birmingham Small Arms Company also staked a claim but then withdrew. Eventually all the contestants lost interest and the quarry was forgotten about until the 1950s when the Admiralty finally occupied it for general storage. Meanwhile the Bristol Aeroplane Company, which had been supportive of the underground factory scheme in its initial stages, suddenly lost enthusiasm and had to be bullied and cajoled into maintaining its participation. Eventually the company agreed to occupy rather less than half of the area allocated to it in Spring Quarry, leaving the Ministry of Aircraft Production with the problem of finding other tenants for the remaining sections which had been acquired and converted at great expense.

The Birmingham Small Arms Company took up a small part of the quarry which was developed as a gun barrel factory, and Parnall Ltd and Dowty agreed to occupy the remainder in which to build, respectively, gun turrets and undercarriage assemblies for Stirling bombers. Both companies subsequently reneged on their agreements and much of Spring Quarry remained unoccupied throughout the war. Ultimately the Spring Quarry project proved to be a shambolic white elephant; construction, which should have been completed within six months, was still unfinished at the end of the war and the factory, despite the £30,000,000 spent on it (against an initial estimate of just £100,000) produced just a negligible number of engines.

It was soon apparent that there would never be enough surplus engines to warrant the retention of Limpley Stoke Quarry, which was subsequently disposed of to the Ministry of Supply who used it, most successfully, to store tens of thousands of tons of high-explosives destined eventually for shell filling factories at Usk, Bridgend and elsewhere in South Wales.

THE ADMIRALTY HAS SECOND THOUGHTS

The Admiralty's attitude towards underground storage, (we have seen already that they were markedly inimical to the concept when the other services were fighting each other for underground capacity in the 1930s), underwent a radical reappraisal in January 1941 after their main Fleet Air Arm stores at Coventry and Woolston were destroyed during air raids. By this time Corsham was a major development area with every service department and a number of primary defence equipment contractors represented there, so it was not surprising that the Admiralty, seeking secure storage, turned its attention there also. It was quickly discovered that Copenacre Quarry, one of the series of working quarries initially requisitioned by the Ministry of Aircraft Production some months earlier but subsequently released, was available. The quarry was immediately requisitioned by the Admiralty and plans prepared on the most lavish scale for its conversion. Elaborate heating, ventilation and transportation equipment was installed and massively proportioned, grossly over-engineered shaft-head buildings erected on the surface. Two long disused quarries at Bradford-on-Avon – Bethel Quarry and Paulton Quarry, both of which had been utilized during the inter-war years as underground mushroom farms – were also requisitioned by the Admiralty at this time.

After the war the Admiralty consolidated its interests at Corsham; the Bradford-on-Avon quarries and the small and inefficient Traveler's Rest and Brockleaze quarries were discarded but Monks Park and the greater part of Spring Quarry were added to its portfolio and survived, along with Copenacre, as the central stores for naval electronic and other specialist equipment throughout the Cold War, finally closing in 1997.

CAD CORSHAM

Initially, the War Office requirement for underground ammunition storage had been quite modest and it was assumed that the six acres available at Ridge Quarry would be sufficient. Almost immediately, however, it was realized that much more extensive accommodation would be required so in August 1935 an agreement was reached with the Bath & Portland Stone Company to purchase both Ridge Quarry and the fifty-acre Tunnel Quarry. Within a few months this too proved insufficient and a further quarry at Eastlays near Gastard was acquired in May 1936. The strengthened plans for the air defence of Great Britain outlined in the early months of 1937 called for much larger reserves of anti-aircraft ammunition than had been earlier anticipated and to meet the storage requirements for this stockpile a further quarry at Monkton Farleigh was purchased in March 1937.

Conversion at both Ridge and Tunnel quarries began simultaneously. The first stage in the process of development was to remove the huge volume of waste stone and debris that had accumulated underground as a result of many decades of quarrying activity. At Tunnel Quarry alone some two million tons of waste stone 'backfill' had to be cleared, a task

Above: The winding engine and boilerhouse at Pickwick quarry (now known as Hartham Park quarry), shortly after the quarry was requisition by the Admiralty for naval ammunition storage. The building and its associated chimney stack still survive beside the Corsham - Fiveways road.

Below: An underground wartime view of Pickwick quarry, showing stacks of Fleet Air Arm bombs.

Above: Naval depth charges stacked underground at Pickwick quarry, with 250lb aerial bombs in the background. As we see here, the roof of many parts of the quarry was lined with asbestos sheeting to drain away the copious amounts of seepage water that found its way into the workings.

Below: Large quantities of Admiralty small-arms ammunition stacked beside the railway line in a corner of the Pickwick Naval Armaments Depot.

Above: A typical view of Pickwick quarry. Immediately after the war the ammunition storage depot was closed down and stocks cleared, and the narrow gauge railway system dismantled. Much of the other wartime infrastructure (which was rather primitive compared with that installed in many of the other quarries), was left in place, including the electric lights, a few of which can be seen in this image.

Left: The principal haulageway through Pickwick quarry, near its innermost end. A large rectangular vertical shaft, positioned just behind the photographer, was the main means by which stocks of ammunition were moved in and out of the quarry.

Above: The winch room which housed the haulage engine operating the main goods lift at Pickwick quarry, still in situ in the middle of a farm-yard. The lift shaft itself was an open structure surrounded by a low brick wall positioned more-or-less where the white-wrapped bales are to the right of this picture.

Below: The winding engine house is in the centre of this aerial view, with an extensive range of more recent farm buildings to the right. The long, low building to the left of the winding engine was the depot's picket post or guardhouse. The large modern complex in the background is the Copenacre Naval Storage Depot.

which took the initial workforce of 12,000 labourers over four years to complete. This task, although overseen at the planning level by a small team of Royal Engineers, was undertaken by a civilian labour force under the administration of a civilian works directorate. Assembly of this workforce was a prodigious affair and was an overt exercise in social engineering organized by the Ministry of Labour. It was decided that unemployed men from the distressed areas of north-east England should be offered employment on the War Office project; transport to Wiltshire would be subsidised by the government and lodgings for every man would be found with a family somewhere within a radius of twenty miles of the works. The concept of containing all these men within the close confines of a labour camp – the usual method of personnel management previously used on large civil engineering projects – was specifically excluded. The high ambition of the War Office was that these men, many of whom had never been in employment, should gradually be weaned into the disciplines of work and that they would become integrated into the culture of the south-west of England. Eventually, it was hoped, they would bring their families down from Durham or Tyneside and start new lives for themselves in Somerset and Wiltshire. At its peak the scheme involved in excess of 25,000 men.

Once the waste stone had been removed the floor throughout the quarries were levelled, the rough roof support pillars left by the quarrymen were strengthened and steel girders put in place to reinforce the overhead cover where necessary. Concrete division walls were built in order to create within each quarry a series of regular, self-contained storage magazines each approximately five acres in extent. Ventilation systems and, later, highly complex air-conditioning plants, were installed in order to maintain satisfactory environmental conditions underground. Vertical lift shafts and smoothly graded inclined shafts were constructed to facilitate ammunition movements and, in total, some twenty miles of conveyor belts put in place and several miles of narrow-gauge railways laid. Tens of thousands of spark-, flame- and explosion-proof electric light fittings were installed and, at the three major sites – Tunnel, Eastlays and Monkton Farleigh – huge standby power stations built underground.

RIDGE QUARRY

Construction work began at Ridge Quarry in July 1936 and was scheduled for completion by the end of December, by which time it was to be ready to receive the first consignment of RAF bombs destined for storage there. Although a War Office depot and nominally a constituent part of Central

Ammunition Depot Corsham, the quarry was handed over, first in part and later as a whole, to the Air Ministry on a supposedly temporary basis. As the Air Ministry's own storage schemes collapsed in disarray as the war progressed, 'temporary' became permanent and Ridge Quarry remained in RAF hands until its closure in 1950.

The requirement to complete the tasks of building and fitting out within six months meant, inevitably, that the engineering works undertaken at Ridge Quarry would be on a modest scale and the facilities provided minimal. Shortly before the arrangement with the Air Ministry was finalized a more comprehensive programme of works had been put in hand but was subsequently abandoned. A start was made on reinforcing the stone support pillars with concrete but this was stopped after no more than one-twentieth of the work was completed when it was realized that it could not be finished within the specified time, that sufficient resources were not economically available and that concentrating labour on this task was delaying more vital work. Unlike the other depots that comprised CAD Corsham, Ridge Quarry was not provided with forced air ventilation or heating, it did not have a dedicated power station (although it did share an emergency electricity supply with the nearby Eastlays depot), and it was never fitted with a permanent, conduit-enclosed electric lighting system.

The one great advantage possessed by Ridge Quarry was that it had been used for explosives storage by the Ministry of Munitions during the latter part of the First World War. The quarry was cleared of debris at that time and the floors levelled. Rails had been laid in the main slope shaft and were still in place in 1936 although the steam winding engine in the surface transit shed and all the narrow-gauge Decauville track underground had been removed at the end of the war. All that was required of the War Office in 1936 was to relay a couple of thousand yards of temporary track, reinstate the winding engine, erect a few division walls and offices underground and install a pretty primitive lighting system with electric cables strung from hooks let into the quarry roof. In order to increase the maximum throughput of ammunition a ventilation shaft situated in the middle of the quarry was adapted for haulage by the installation of a simple, double-cage lift running in timber guides.

In 1942, at the request of the Air Ministry, the capacity of Ridge Quarry was substantially increased by the re-opening of a long-disused slope shaft at the west end of the quarry that gave convenient access to further areas of underground workings. Due to the presence of a geological fault that runs through the quarry these extended workings are at a level some twenty feet below the main area, so a pair of inclined passages were bored to connect the two parts of the quarry. Winches were installed at the head of each underground incline, powered by small steam engines adapted to run on compressed air, the air being provided by two compressors on the surface. The passageway linking the 'new' inclined shaft to the existing workings ran through an area of treacherous ground and the engineering in this area is noticeably heavier than in other areas of the quarry, with many substantial concrete walls and large steel girders supporting the roof.

Storage conditions at Ridge Quarry were barely adequate and the weapons stored there – mainly obsolete American bombs delivered early in the war – deteriorated dangerously. All were finally removed during a delicate operation in 1949; the following year the Air Ministry terminated its occupation and the site reverted to War Office control. Ridge was never used again although it was kept on minimal care and maintenance until 1964 when the Army, too, abandoned the site. The quarry was eventually sold in 1975 to the Neston Estate from whom it had been purchased in 1935. Soon after, rails and many of the roof support girders underground were recovered for scrap, leaving some areas of the quarry in a precarious state. Most of the surface features were demolished including the lift-top building and the transit shed at the head of the main inclined shaft. Debris was bulldozed into the shafts and there is now no evidence of their surface location. The loading platform at the top of the new or No.2 slope shaft of 1942 survives at the time of writing, and the slope shaft is still visible and was, until recently, open and accessible.

Below: A load of already obsolete RAF bombs arriving at No.1 loading platform at Ridge Quarry in 1941

Above: No.2 loading platform at Ridge quarry, one of the depot's only surviving surface buildings (the others are a small wooden shed housing the incoming 11,000 Volt power supply and the semi-underground emergency operations room). The right hand bay of this building, just out of frame of this picture, housed a steam winch used to haul trucks up the inclined shaft.

Below: A view out from the end of No.2 loading platform towards the shaft top building (now obscured by a stack of large stone blocks).

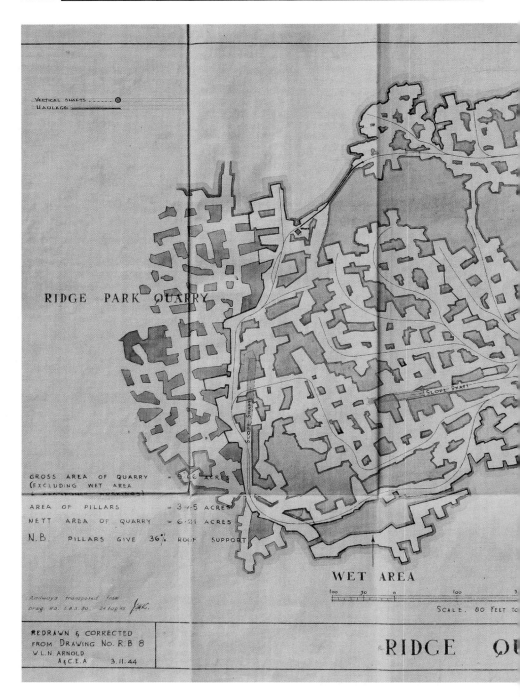

VERTICAL SHAFTS .... ⊕
HAULAGE ————————

RIDGE PARK QUARRY

GROSS AREA OF QUARRY = 9·16 ACRES
(EXCLUDING WET AREA
& ABANDONED WORKINGS)
AREA OF PILLARS = 3·45 ACRES
NETT AREA OF QUARRY = 6·31 ACRES
N.B. PILLARS GIVE 36% ROOF SUPPORT

*Railways transposed from
Drwg. No. S.B.S. 80. 24.10.45.*

REDRAWN & CORRECTED
FROM DRAWING No. R.B 8
W.L.N. ARNOLD
A&C.E.A   3.11.44

SLOPE SHAFT
SLOPE SHAFT

WET AREA

100 50 0 100
SCALE. 80 FEET TO

RIDGE QU

80

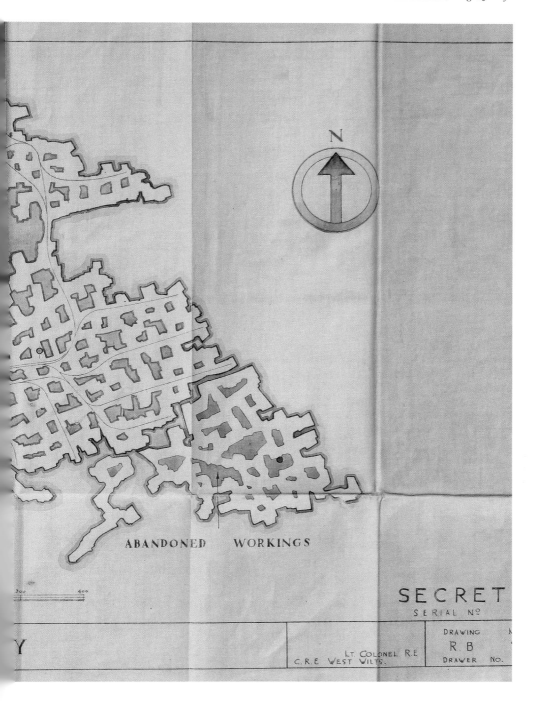

ABANDONED   WORKINGS

SECRET
SERIAL Nº

Lt. COLONEL R.E
C.R.E WEST WILTS.

DRAWING
R B
DRAWER   No.

Above: A view down the derelict remains of Ridge quarry No.2 slope shaft. A single line of narrow gauge rails was laid on the right hand side of the shaft, but these were taken for scrap in the late 1960s.

Below: The bottom of No.2 slope shaft. Here, like elsewhere in the quarry, many of the substantial steel girders put in during the war to reinforce the roof were ill-advisedly removed for scrap in the 1960s.

Above: A fairly typical view in Ridge quarry. The concrete block with four hold-down bolts seen in the foreground once supported a steam capstan, adapted for running on compressed air, used for moving ammunition trucks around on the quarry railway.

Below: A geological fault runs through Ridge quarry, resulting in one half of the quarry being on a lower level than the other. This is one of the two inclined passages, worked by haulage engines, joining the two levels.

Above: It was initially planned to reinforce the whole of Ridge quarry with massive concrete walls and pillars, as seen here, but ultimately the urgency to bring the depot quickly into service resulted in much of this scheme being abandoned.

Below: In this view we some of the concrete reinforcement work in the foreground while in the background a large area of the quarry is in its original state.

Above: One of the concrete reinforced pillars left in an unfinished state when the decision was taken to abandon the original scheme and rely instead on the existing quarry pillars to provide adequate support.

Below: The bottom of No.1 slope shaft at Ridge quarry. During its working life this was the main entrance although it is now completely blocked at the surface and no trace of it remains. The depot's offices and power distribution room were situated between the pillars on the right of the shaft.

EASTLAYS

With the administration of Ridge Quarry transferred to the Air Ministry, the organization of CAD Corsham was restructured. Ridge became a satellite of the much larger Eastlays depot which was under construction nearby. Physically, and for operational purposes, the three main quarries which comprised the Central Ammunition Depot – Eastlays, Tunnel Quarry and Monkton Farleigh – were divided into a series of twenty-five separate storage magazines or 'districts' each of approximately five acres in extent and numbered consecutively. Districts 1-11 were to be at Tunnel Quarry, 12-20 at Monkton Farleigh and 21-25 at Eastlays. Confusingly, the depots themselves were given a number sequence that did not correspond to the district numbering sequence. Hence Tunnel Quarry was classified as Sub-depot No.1 with Districts 1-11, but Eastlays, nominated Sub-depot No.2 contained Districts 21-25. Sub-depot No.3 at Monkton Farleigh was home to Districts 12-20. There is no rational explanation of this numbering system; it reflects neither the order in which the quarries were purchased, built or brought into service. There is a further slight complication that District No.1 at Tunnel Quarry does not exist because the area in which it was to have been built was abandoned as unsafe after construction had begun, and District No.13 at Monkton Farleigh is absent solely for reasons of superstition.

Work started on the conversion of Eastlays in July 1936 but progress was at first held back by the urgent need to complete the preparation of Ridge Quarry for the RAF. Thereafter, the escalating storage requirements of the RAF caused constant changes to be made to the design of the Eastlays depot. Although conceived as a primary element of the army's central ammunition supply chain, Eastlays, in fact, did not play a role in this organization until the very end of the Second World War when it was used as the principal reception point for surplus ammunition returned from the various theatres of war.

Before its acquisition by the War Office, Eastlays Quarry was a rambling network of headings and working faces severely congested by waste stone debris. The only access was via an awkwardly placed, narrow and very steep inclined shaft that dropped into the middle of the workings. The War Office engineers realized from the outset that this shaft would not be suitable for ammunition movements in the completed depot so one of their first tasks was to arrange for two new, more favourably graded inclines to be sunk at each end of the quarry. Once the debris had been cleared it was found that the pillars supporting the roof had been dangerously undercut by the quarrymen in an attempt to extract the last easily accessible stone from underground, and that as a consequence the whole quarry was somewhat unstable. In order to stabilize the structure the War Office was compelled to build very extensive concrete walls and pillars, making Eastlays by far the most heavily engineered of the Corsham quarries.

Work progressed from west to east and even before District No.21 at the far west of the depot was completed in August 1939, arrangements had been made with the Ministry of Supply for it to be used for the storage of bulk TNT destined for the bomb filling factories then under construction. In May 1940, District No.22, the next to be completed, was also transferred to the MoS for the storage of 40,000 tons of cordite. By the end of the month the two completed districts were issuing in excess of 2,000 tons of high-explosives weekly to the filling factories. District No.23, completed in October 1940, was very quickly filled with bulk TNT and in December the recently completed Districts 24 and 25 were handed over to the RAF for the storage of bomb and small-arms ammunition.

To handle receipts and issues of bulk explosives, which was delivered in small packages, the original War Office electric belt conveyor was retained in No.1 slope shaft. At the east end of the depot, No.2 shaft, which fed the bomb stores in Districts 24 and 25, was fitted with a winch and narrow-gauge rails to handle the heavier weapons stored there. Underground, the Air Ministry provided Ransom Rapier battery electric trucks for movements within the magazines.

The storage of cordite and TNT underground presented problems that had not been envisaged when the original scheme for the Corsham depots was drawn up. The underground depots were designed for use in wartime, and solely for the storage of field service ammunition – bullets, mortars and artillery projectiles – all of which were sturdy, weather-proof items that could withstand a degree of mishandling. Moreover, because the depots were designed as essentially temporary wartime exigencies, it was expected that the materials stored underground would turn over very quickly, the quarries acting as no more than transit depots between armament factory and battlefield. Cordite and TNT, however, are sensitive, unstable substances liable to degradation if atmospheric conditions are not maintained within a limited range of temperature and humidity. It was necessary, for the safe storage of propellants and high-explosives, to equip Districts 21, 22 and 23 with sophisticated air-conditioning, heating and ventilation apparatus to ensure the necessary conditions were maintained. The plant at Eastlays was at the time of its construction one of the most complex in the western hemisphere.

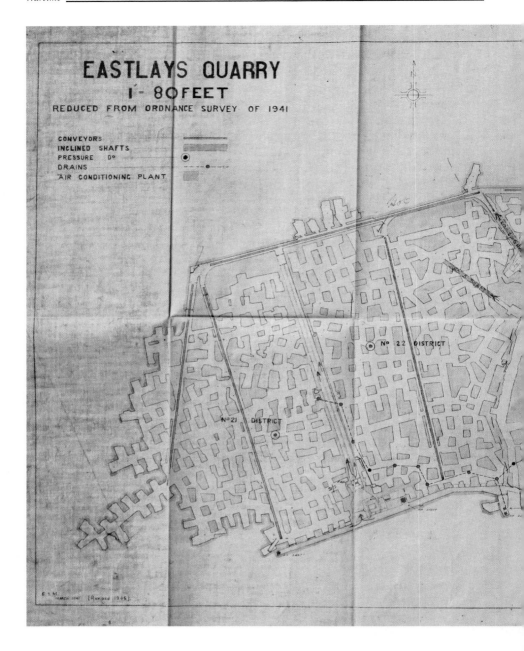

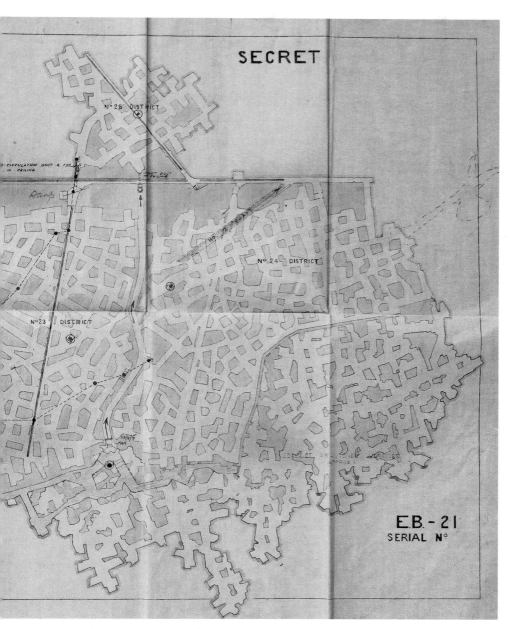

Above: Eastlays quarry, showing the distribution of support pillars, roadways, ventilation shafts and storage 'Districts' of the completed ammunition storage depot. Notice that a large area of some five acres to the south east of the quarry have been walled-off and isolated due to the fact that it was found impossible to control the ingress of seepage water to this part of the quarry.

Above: No.1 entrance building to the Eastlays ammunition depot. This was the main entrance and was designed specifically for handling large RAF bombs. Within the surface loading platform there was an overhead rail-mounted crane for transferring bombs from lorries onto narrow-gauge railway trucks. These trucks were then lowered underground by means of a powerful electric winch. The concrete section seen in this image is part of the original structure; since the site was taken over as a bonded warehouse in the 1980s the previously open loafing platform has been enclosed in corrugated steel sheeting.

Right: By contrast, No.2 entrance was a simple wooden structure housing a loading bay and a rubber belt conveyor used to transport smaller, boxed ammunition underground. By the time this (rather poor) photo was taken in 1984 the building had collapsed, leaving only the concrete portal to the inclined slope shaft visible.

Above: Since the photograph opposite, of No.1 entrance, was taken in the year 2000, there has been much development work at the bonded warehouse and a new surface building has been erected, more-or-less enclosing the original concrete structure.

Below: No.2 entrance too, is now unrecognisable from its wartime appearance with this new, steel clad, steel framed lorry loading bay and office block.

Above: A consignment of American made 1000 lb, and *(below)* 250 lb General Purpose High Explosive bombs being stacked underground in No.24 District at Eastlays during the Second World War.

Above: A bay full of 250 lb bombs in store at Eastlays. What can be seen in this photograph represents about one-thousandth of the total stock-holding in the depot.

Below: Raw TNT in boxes, manufactured in America by the Tennessee Powder Company, being stacked in Eastlays. About 40,000 of TNT was stored on behalf of the Ministry of Supply in the depot at any one time, destined ultimately for bomb-filling factories in South Wales.

Above: Boxes of small-arms ammunition from the Remington Arms Company of America being stacked in Eastlays quarry. All of the bombs, explosives and other American made ammunition seen in this and the preceding photographs was delivered under the Lend-Lease programme, and the photographs were taken primarily for publication in the American press as propaganda in support of the programme.

Above: In addition to the two main goods entrances at Eastlays there was a third, shown above, known as the Engineer's Shaft which descended into the plant area of the quarry housing the standby generator, maintenance stores and workshop etc. Although almost completely weathered away, this building was once adorned with striking quasi-Germanic camouflage dating from 1983 when it was used as a film set for the BBC drama *'The Fourth Arm'*.

Below: A view up the Engineer's Shaft showing the Warwick beam which was mechanically interlocked with a lifting barrier at the bottom of the shaft and was designed as a safety measure to arrest a runaway truck on the shaft.

Above: The main haulageway in the plant area of the quarry. The lifting barrier at the bottom of the access shaft (on the right of this image) is the co-acting part of the Warwick beam shown on the previous page.

Below: The powerhouse at Eastlays with its single, Blackstone Brush supercharged 8M9P eight-cylinder horizontally opposed diesel engine and alternator set.

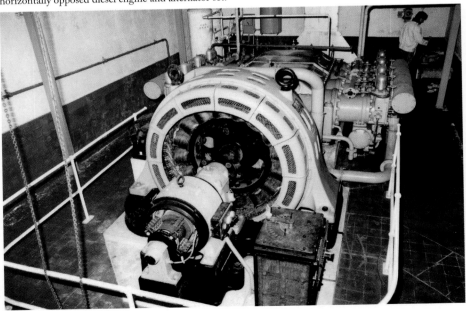

Left: The generator control equipment in the powerhouse at Eastlays. The plant here is much simpler than that installed at the two other CAD Corsham depots (Tunnel Quarry & Monkton Farleigh) as only one generator and one incoming mains feed were installed.

The tall group of instruments mounted on an orange painted base is the station's synchronizing column, the use of which ensures that when the mains supply and generator output are running in tandem, the three phases are synchronized.

The left hand panel monitors the output of the alternator while the right hand panel controls the output from the transformer to the low voltage (415V) distribution panels.

Below: Since the mid-1980s Eastlays has been used as a high security bonded warehouse storing both commercial stocks of alcohol and several very valuable private collections of wine, the stable atmospheric condition underground making the site perfect for this function. This view, taken near the base of No.1 inclined shaft, shows a train of wagons loaded with wine boxes that has been lowered down the shaft and is now awaiting transfer to storage.

TUNNEL QUARRY

Tunnel Quarry was the largest and operationally most flexible of the sub-depots that made up CAD Corsham. The flexibility was due to the characteristics of the old quarry workings within which it was constructed. To the north of the site Huddswell Quarry had been worked via a pair of vertical winding shafts, while the southern section of the quarry adjacent to Box railway tunnel had the advantage of being served by a railway branch line that entered into the heart of the workings. A steep incline, No.7 shaft, also penetrated the quarry from the surface; this shaft was used during construction but was blocked and abandoned in 1941. The Huddswell lift shafts, on the other hand, were refurbished and fitted with locally fabricated lift cages to transport large artillery shells. The lifts were powered for the first couple of years by an improvised steam winch until replaced by a permanent installation of 30 cwt Herbert Morris double-cage lifts in December 1940.

Underground, the stone-loading platform was replaced by an impressive double-platform underground station connected to the extremities of the storage areas by eleven miles of conveyor belts. The underground station was brought into service in October 1939. Meanwhile, on the surface directly above the station, work was advancing on the construction of the Main Surface Loading Platform or MSLP. This building, partially buried into the hillside, consisted of four lorry loading bays that fed, via short conveyors, into a hexagonal rear chamber from which radiated four inclined shafts descending into distant areas of the quarry. The MSLP became operational towards the end of 1941.

Tunnel Quarry is part of a network of workings encompassing more than 100 acres of underground space. Tunnel Quarry is to the north of the Box railway tunnel and Spring Quarry to the south. At the eastern end of the workings the railway tunnel and the quarry workings are at the same level, but as one travels to the west the inclination of the stone strata rises while the tunnel dips so that a little beyond the western extremity of the underground station the railway is below the quarry workings. The GWR was concerned that, over the length of tunnel where railway and ammunition depot were on the same level, precautions were taken to ensure that an accidental explosion in the depot would not pose a risk to their tunnel. To ensure safety a twenty-foot thick concrete barrier was erected along the whole length of the southern extremity of the depot. Tunnel Quarry was conceived as a completely self-contained bomb proof structure with all its vital facilities safely concealed beneath one hundred feet of rock. Just north of the underground station the Royal Engineers built a locomotive shed where the three War Office standard-gauge diesel locomotives were stabled and serviced; close by was an underground powerhouse containing two Ruston 5VLB diesel generating sets; a little to the west was an office complex housing all the administrative facilities that one would normally expect to find on a conventional army depot including a telephone exchange, while further to the west there were barracks for 300 men. The latter fell into disuse in 1942 when the threat from German bombing had become insignificant.

Adequate ventilation of the depot was a problem that taxed the ingenuity of the Royal Engineers for many years. At first it was hoped that natural ventilation, aided by an induction fan sucking air from the surface, would suffice. Whilst this system kept the air below ground relatively fresh it did little to improve the high humidity and consequent condensation in the magazines. The second stage of the ventilation scheme involved the erection of a 160-inch diameter fan – the largest fan in any of the Corsham quarries – at the far west end of the depot at which point it drew in air via Brewer's Drift and the Wind Tunnel from the old quarry workings on the perimeter of the depot. The hope was that, in its transit from outside the quarries to the fan through half-a-mile or more of subterranean passageways, air drawn into the depot would deposit most of its water content in the old workings before reaching the fan. This system, too, failed to live up to its expectations.

Experimentally, a small boiler was set up underground providing steam that heated radiators placed in the inlet air ducts for No.2 District. Air was blown into the district through the radiators by means of a dedicated fan and extracted by a second fan placed at the top of the district's outlet shaft. Adequate conditions were produced by this pilot installation and encouraged the War Office to prepare plans for a large-scale heating system for the whole depot. Steam for this system would be provided by a boiler house situated in a surface compound north of the MSLP, completed in late 1944.

When the CAD scheme was first proposed it was assumed that the maximum daily issue of ammunition would be no more than 2,000 tons. The underground platforms and the MSLP were each designed to cope with this capacity, with the MSLP intended as a reserve capacity in the event of a breakdown of the railway system. Throughout the early war years these maximum figures were never attained; practice showed that the most efficient means of supplying the field army was to ship ammunition direct from ordnance factory to port for onward dispatch to the theatre of war, completely bypassing the reserve depots. When it was necessary to hold stock for short periods of time this was generally undertaken at surface ammunition depots having basic facilities or by the use of temporary roadside dumps. Thus, the reserve depots tended gradually to accumulate stocks of slow-moving and obsolete ammunition. Things changed, however, during the preparations for D-Day when huge volumes of ammunition of all types started to arrive at Corsham. Turnover of fresh stocks during April and May 1944 amounted to 32,000 tons, while 10,500 tons were issued during the last week of June with comparable quantities shipped during the weeks thereafter.

Although planned as a temporary wartime expedient, CAD Corsham was later reclassified as a permanent depot and continued to function for almost twenty years after the end of the Second World War, with regular supplies being made to British units in the Far and Middle East and to forces engaged in the Korean War. The end finally came on 4 December 1962 when, as a consequence of the defence review of that year, the depot was finally closed. It has, however, for almost fifty years remained in the hands of the Ministry of Defence under care and maintenance.

Below: Conversion work under way at Tunnel Quarry in 1938. Here we see the concrete arch giving access to the underground railway platforms under construction. Old tramway rails from the Bath tram system are being used as reinforcements for the concrete.

Above: The main line railway entrance to Tunnel quarry, with a War Office diesel shunter drawing an ammunition train into the depot via the War Office tunnel immediately to the north of, and parallel to, the east portal of Box railway tunnel.

Below: The main surface loading platform (MSLP) for Tunnel quarry, near Basil Hill, seen here in 1944.

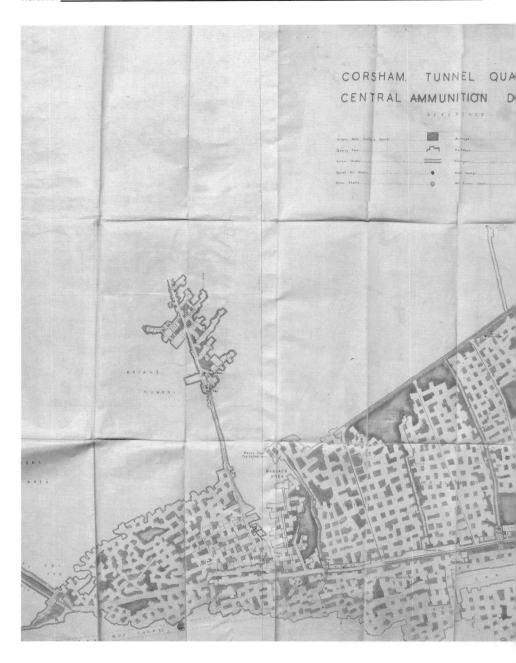

Above: Plan of Tunnel quarry, drawn up by Fred Allen, who was Civilian Engineer In Chief overseeing the whole of the War Office construction programme at Corsham since 1936. The blue lines on the right hand half of the plan shows the standard-gauge railway lines, including the long eastern storage siding, two platform lines and the underground engine shed that housed the three War Office shunting locomotives.

Above: The eastern portal of Brunel's Box tunnel, with the lower and much less ornate portal of the War Office tunnel. This tunnel, which was originally constructed by the Yockney & Hartham Park Stone Company in 1876 to give direct access to their workings, was much enlarged by the War Office.

Below: A closer view of the gates securing access to the underground platforms at Tunnel quarry. Although the siding and connections to the main line were dismantled in the 1967, all the rails remain in place on the far side of the gate.

Above: This view shows a section of the War Office tunnel looking back out towards the entrance. Note the standard gauge track laid in concrete. The points just visible in the middle distance, at the end of the left-hand concrete wall, gives access to a long storage siding. The main line Box tunnel is to the right, separated by about twenty-feet of virgin stone.

Below: In this view we are looking into the depot, with the right-hand line heading towards the engine shed and the left hand line heading towards the underground station. Here the main line tunnel is behind the concrete wall on the left.

Above: The eastern section of the north loading platform at Tunnel quarry, looking out towards the tunnel entrance. The building at the top of the steel steps is the control room controlling the eleven miles of belt conveyor in the depot.

Below: The same platform looking west, into the depot. Note the rails laid in concrete on the right and the ammunition conveyor on the left.

Above: A bridge underground! This is Tunnel quarry's Main East haulageway, which burrows beneath the railway lines serving the loading platforms. The bridge in the middle distance carries power cables over the haulageway while the bridge in the background carries two standard gauge railway lines.

Below: The entrance to the underground engine shed where the depot's three diesel shunters were serviced.

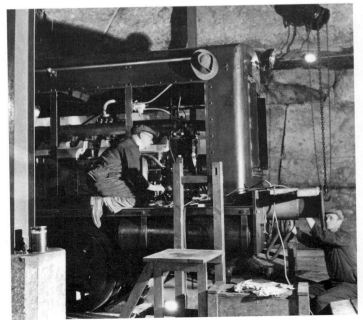

Above: inside the engine shed, with the inspection pit in the foreground and the turntable serving the three storage roads in the background.

Left: One of the depot's Hunslet shunters undergoing routine maintenance in 1944.

Opposite below: A plan of the Main Surface Loading Platform showing the four inclined shafts radiating from the inner chamber.

Above: Tunnel quarry's Main Surface Loading Platform, now somewhat obscured by undergrowth. Compare this with the wartime image on page 101.

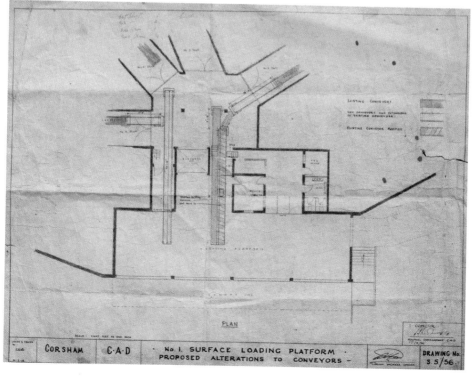

Above: The top of No.5 shaft in the MSLP today with a truck load of rubbish being brought to the surface.

Below: Looking up No.5 shaft; originally there was a conveyor belt on the left hand side of the steps (see opposite). The steelwork on the right consists of safety stops for the wagon haulage system.

Above: No.5 shaft, seen shortly after commissioning. There is an ammunition conveyor on the left and a runway for a wagon haulage system on the right. Towards the top of the shaft the inclination of the wagon haulage increases so that the wagons terminate on a floor above the conveyor system, from where they are lowered to the working floor by a short elevator.

Left: Ammunition boxes from a conveyor on the railway platform (on the left) being transferred to the conveyor in No.5 shaft for despatch by lorry.

Left: A consignment of 5-inch shells arriving in the depot via the conveyor in No.2 inclined shaft. A short mobile conveyor unit is being used to route the shells into No.5 storage District.

Below: Two main haulageways, (Main East and Main West), link all the storage Districts to the railway platforms. Each of the main haulageways has two conveyors, a High Belt and a Low Belt, so arranged that both issues and receipts of ammunition can be done simultaneously. Here we see an issue of anti-tank mines being transferred from No.5 District to the the Low Belt.

Above & below: Two typical views of field gun ammunition stored in Tunnel quarry. Each of these images show just one small corner of one of a large number of bays in one District. There are ten 'Districts' in the depot, each extending over about five acres and holding a total of some 120,000 tons of ammunition.

Left: A stream of 5" field gun shells being unloaded from the conveyor in No.5 District ready to be transferred by hand-truck to their designated storage bay.

Below: Ammunition for the 18" Railway Howitzer, relics of the First World War that were never fired in anger, and nor did they see action in the Second World War. Manufactured in 1918, the entire stock was dumped in the Irish Sea in 1965.

Left: This is No.6 District at Tunnel quarry, stacked to the ceiling with 25-pounder propellant charges. The District is a quarter of a mile long and the storage bays extend back over 100-feet on either side of the conveyor. There is approximately 25,000 tons of explosives stacked in this District.

Right: Stacking 25-pounder HE projectiles in No.6 District. Notice that in this wartime photograph the work is being done by civilian rather than military personnel; presumably men too old to be conscripted into the fighting services.

Above: As well as the railway platforms and the MSLP, there was a further means of access to Tunnel quarry in the form of two vertical lifts in the old Huddswell shaft. These were used for the handling of large shells, too heavy for the conveyor system, arriving by lorry. This image shows the bottom of the lift shaft and the haulage engine used to transport ammunition too and from the lifts.

Huddswell Drift, viewed from the haulage engine platform. This passage stretches along the northern perimeter of the depot, communicating with all of the western storage Districts. Wagons in the drift were propelled by an overhead rope haulage system.

Left: Another view of Huddswell Drift, showing a number of empty ammunition wagons and a couple attached to the haulage cable, loaded with 9.2" shells.

Below: When the depot was first commissioned all ammunition transfers were made using a system of narrow-gauge rails and overhead haulage equipment. This, however, was found to be too inflexible, noisy and dangerous and by 1942 most had been replaced by conveyors. This early photo shows the original setup in No.2 District.

Above: The remains of the Huddswell haulage engine today, together with a small group of derelict ammunition trucks. Note the rusty lift cages immediately behind the trucks.

Below: A Huddswell ammunition truck fitted with a cage for securing an 18" howitzer shell.

Above: Main West haulageway, serving Districts 2, 3, 4, 10 & 11. Two conveyors, a High Belt and Low Belt, were provided in this roadway but were transferred to Monkton Farleigh quarry in 1985.

Below: The disused conveyor belt in No.6 District. The number on the wall refers to Bay 182 in No.6 District.

Above & below: Two views of the conveyor belts in Districts 3 and 4. In total, some eleven miles of interlinked conveyor served the various storage areas.

Above: Near the bottom of No.2 incline today, with the Main East conveyors to the far left and the link conveyor to No.5 District in the foreground. Compare this scene to the wartime images of the same location on page 112.

Below: The bottom of No.4 shaft in No.11 District. The bells and push-buttons on the right hand wall control the operation of the conveyors, the bells transmitting start / stop instructions from the MSLP.

Above: A front view of the two Ruston Hornsby VLB5 generator sets in the powerhouse at Tunnel quarry.

Below: The rear of No.1 generator, showing the red, asbestos clad exhaust connection which is carried to the surface via an underfloor duct and dedicated vertical shaft.

Above: The powerhouse switch-room at Tunnel quarry. The group of black panels consist of two generator panels, two exciter panels, two HV transformer panels and a bus-bar panel. There was once a chrome 'BTH' maker's plate and a Smiths electric clock over the centre of this unit.

Left: A wider view of the switch-room, with more modern 11Kv switchgear in the foreground. The wartime HV transformers were housed in the caged enclosure in the background.

Left: When the initial plans were prepared for the construction of Tunnel quarry, it was envisioned that ventilation air would be drawn in via a passageway known as Brewer's Drift from the vast network of disused quarry workings to the west of the depot, and that while passing through these workings the air would give up most of its natural moisture due to the stable, low temperature environment of the quarry workings. By this means it was hoped to avoid the cost of expensive dehumidification plant in the ammunition store. This plan, however, was only partially effective and ultimately a complex system of air heating and dehumidification plant was installed at considerable expense.

This photograph shows the C.D.I (Corsham Depot Inlet) fan, which was a feature of the original scheme and was designed to draw some 400,000 cubic feet of air per minute into the depot from the Box quarries.

THINGLEY JUNCTION

A feature of CAD Corsham was that all its sub-depots should primarily receive and issue stock by rail, so plans were laid at an early stage to provide railheads as close as possible to each sub-depot. Although Tunnel Quarry had its own underground station this was not large enough to handle long, trains of mixed cargoes, such as whole, ship-load consignments of imported ammunition from the docks or outward cargoes for a supply convoy to a distant battlefield. Inward shipments would be distributed throughout the Corsham sub-depots and, similarly, large outward shipments would be assembled from items stored in the various sub-depots. Eastlays and Monkton Farleigh quarries had their own dedicated rail terminals similar in function to the underground station at Tunnel Quarry; Eastlays at Beanacre sidings a mile away by road, and Monkton Farleigh at Farleigh Down Sidings near Box, connected to the quarry by a spectacular one-and-a-quarter mile long tunnel. All three sub-depots were served by an extensive new reception, assembly and distribution yard constructed in 1938 for the War Office by the GWR at Thingley Junction near Chippenham, where the former Wilts, Somerset & Weymouth line branches off south towards Trowbridge.

Above: Thingley Junction, still busy in 1952, presumably despatching ammunition for the Korean War.

Below: Thingley Junction in 1986. The shed and platforms were erected when it was proposed to use the yard for freight transfers for the Admiralty storage facilities in Corsham, but the upgraded yard saw little if any use. In more recent years it saw a brief burst of activity as a construction depot in connection with the ill fated London-Bristol railway overhead electrification scheme.

BROWN'S QUARRY

Early in 1940 the RAF decided to establish a secure underground operations centre for No.10 Group, Fighter Command in the Corsham quarries. It was understood that construction of the underground facility would not be completed until the early part of 1941 so, as an interim measure, Rudloe Manor near Box was requisitioned as temporary accommodation in June 1940. Staff and administrative functions were housed in the mansion while a makeshift control room and associated facilities were established in huts in the grounds.

The underground operations centre was constructed in Brown's Quarry, a remote heading north of Tunnel Quarry but connected to it by a long, narrow passage. Construction was completed in December 1940 and the site handed over to the RAF on 15 January 1941. Access was by means of a passenger lift from the surface, although there was also an emergency link to Tunnel Quarry via the underground heading. This passage also gave access to South West Control, an RAF telecommunications centre controlling voice and teleprinter links between airfields and other establishments in the south-west of England. South West Control was constructed in what had been earmarked as Tunnel Quarry's No.1 ammunition storage district, but which had been abandoned when the Royal Engineers decided that the roof structure was dangerously unstable. It would appear, however, that different safety criteria were applied by the RAF who went ahead with construction despite War Office misgivings.

Brown's Quarry continued in its role as No.10 Group Operations Centre until 1945 when the Group was disbanded and the site became home to the RAF Control and Reporting School. In 1950 it took on a new lease of life as the Southern Sector Control for the RAF's Rotor radar system. Rotor was an immensely complex and hugely expensive radar network intended to provide a nation-wide shield against Russian atomic bombers. Unfortunately the concept of manned bombers and atomic bombs gave way to ballistic missiles and nuclear warheads – against which there could be no active defence – and the whole Rotor project, along with the Corsham operations centre, was abandoned in 1958 before the scheme achieved its final fruition. Military communications facilities under different guises continued to operate underground in the Corsham quarries but by 1980 the wartime operations room was long abandoned and is now just an empty shell.

Above: No.10 Group Operations Room in Brown's quarry, on an apparently busy day in 1943. The WAAF girls move tallies on the plotting table to mark the positions, strength and direction of movements of British fighters and enemy aircraft while Officers on the mezzanine floors direct events, issue commands to the pilots, receive information from Royal Observer Corps units , radar stations and other locations, and liaise with anti-aircraft sites within their Sector.

Left: No.10 Group Operations Room, looking down from the Mezzanine onto the plotting table. The outline of the area controlled by the Sector can be seen on the map.

Below: By the mid-1980s the Operations Room had been disused and abandoned for some two decades and rot had taken hold of the wooden structure supporting the mezzanine floors, so the decision was made to demolish the entire structure, leaving just the concrete shell and a few odd brick walls.

MONKTON FARLEIGH QUARRY

Although Monkton Farleigh quarry is a few miles from the town of Corsham, we will include a brief description and just a few photographs in this book as it did form Sub-Depot No. 3 of Central Ammunition Depot Corsham, and the story would not be complete without some mention of it.

Monkton Farleigh Quarry was acquired in the latter months of 1937 to provide additional storage space for army field ammunition and, more importantly, anti-aircraft ammunition for the air defence of the United Kingdom. As the impending war grew closer the vulnerability of the United Kingdom to aerial attack became increasingly apparent and the role of Anti-Aircraft Command rose higher upon the defence agenda.

With the experience of construction difficulties at the earlier Corsham depots behind them, the War Office developed a more sophisticated scheme for Monkton Farleigh Quarry. Instead of adapting the existing random layout of quarry pillars, these would all be swept away to be replaced by regularly spaced concrete walls and pillars to produce a subterranean complex consisting of six rectangular boxes each 1,420 feet long, 180 feet wide and eleven feet high. Each box, or magazine, would be separated from those adjacent by twin, concrete-walled passageways which would serve as protective blast barriers, ventilation ducts and emergency escape corridors. It was realized that this form of construction would take longer to complete but, at Monkton Farleigh, the War Office had the advantage that the area of quarry earmarked for development was surrounded by some fifty further acres of quarry which had been part of the original purchase but were surplus to the initial requirement. Two five-acre sections of these spare workings to the west of the main area, known as 'K' and 'L' areas, (later 19 and 20 Districts respectively), were quickly adapted to a minimal standard to provide temporary storage until the main works were complete. Both were provided with independent incline shafts to the surface for access. 'K' area was commissioned in May 1937 and 'L' area four months later in September. Meanwhile, more than 2,000 men were put to work in No. 12 District, the first of the permanent magazines to be completed.

Monkton Farleigh was unusual amongst the Corsham quarries in that, although the workings were 100 feet below the surface, they were burrowed below the top of a high ridge almost 600 feet above sea level. The principal route for issues and receipts of ammunition was via a railway yard at Farleigh Down Sidings in the valley below. Plans had been prepared in December 1938 for the construction of a one-and-a-quarter mile long tunnel to link the sidings with the main depot but, as it was expected that this might take three years to complete, an aerial ropeway was constructed as a temporary expedient. A terminal building on the hilltop served the surface loading platforms for Districts 19 and 20, while an intermediate station near the unfinished Main West entrance building provided access to No. 12 District via a temporary lift erected in the district's ventilation exhaust shaft.

No. 12 District was completed and handed over to the Royal Ordnance Corps in March 1940. Buoyed by the success of its quite complex engineering, the Royal Engineers decided upon an even more radical design for No. 14 District which involved the complete removal of all the natural stone in the entire area and its replacement by a series of four-foot-thick lateral walls crossing the district and spaced at twenty-two-foot intervals. The walls would be pierced with a series of arches to allow freedom of movement and ventilation, and the middle arches in each wall would form a central access way in which would be placed a belt conveyor. Between each pair of walls pre-stressed reinforced concrete beams – experimental in design and the first to be used in the United Kingdom – were attached to steel corbels let into the tops of the walls, spanning the gap in order to support the ceilings in each bay. Development of the district started well but the rush to finish, together with the employment of inexperienced labour, caused the various stages of construction to become unsynchronized resulting in a serious roof collapse. It was then decided to abandon this advanced method of construction and revert to the system of ad-hoc pillar strengthening used elsewhere in the depots. By the middle of 1941 the War Office priority had changed with respect to Monkton Farleigh. The idea of utilizing the temporary areas to relieve pressure on the depot while the permanent districts were completed to an exceptionally high standard gave way to a policy of finishing everything as quickly as possible and incorporating the hitherto 'temporary' sections as part of the permanent storage facility. Instead of stripping out the random arrangement of pillars left by the quarrymen in the lower end of the depot the engineers arranged, as far as possible, to take advantage of the existing layout. In this way the work was completed both expeditiously and economically. Towards the end of the war and into the 1950s, when operational pressure upon the depots had eased, a programme of further pillar strengthening and other improvements was begun at Monkton Farleigh.

Amongst the new, post-war works was a plan to fully air-condition the whole of the depot. Throughout the war the underground areas had been heated and ventilated by a system of steam radiators and twelve-foot diameter circulating fans. Induction fans were positioned in underground chambers at the east end of each district with extraction fans at the tops of exhaust air-shafts at the west end. Steam was provided by a surface boiler house containing four large Lancashire boilers. While this made working conditions underground tolerable it did little to reduce the overall level of humidity, which was a more insidious evil. Although obsolete ammunition tended to accumulate in the underground reserve depots to some extent, during the war years there was generally a constant turnover of stock so very little ammunition was kept below ground long enough for it to be detrimentally effected by the environmental conditions. Post-war, however, when the depots were reclassified as long-term storage, dealing with the humidity became more of a problem and it was for this reason that full air-conditioning was installed at great expense at Monkton Farleigh. This installation was intended to be an experiment, the results of which would determine the new plants that would subsequently be installed at Eastlays and Tunnel Quarry. However, soon after the system was started up in 1955 problems developed with the structure of the quarry. Whilst the dry, warm air from the conditioning plant produced perfect storage conditions for ammunition, it also dried out both the natural rock and the clay layers bonding the various stone strata in the quarry, resulting in roof falls and fractured pillars. The cost of rectifying these problems, by a massive programme of pillar strengthening, proved prohibitive and hastened the demise of the depots in the 1960s.

In 1974 Monkton Farleigh and Eastlays were sold into the private sector and were earmarked by their new owners for development as underground mushroom farms. These plans did not come to fruition and Monkton Farleigh, being somewhat out on a limb, was quietly abandoned to the depredations of vandals and scrap metal thieves.

In 1984 the by now badly vandalised quarry was acquired by the author of this book and, with the help of a group of dedicated volunteers, much of the depot was restored more-or-less to its wartime condition, over a period of six years. Help was received from the government's Property Services Agency, which by then was the principal custodian of Tunnel Quarry at Corsham, and many artefacts from Tunnel Quarry, which would never have been accessible to the general public, were transferred from Corsham to Monkton Farleigh for restoration and display.

By 1990 the costs of maintaining Monkton Farleigh quarry proved prohibitive and it closed to the public and was once again trashed by vandals. In recent years, however the quarry has found renewed life as a secure storage facility although many of the original features have been lost.

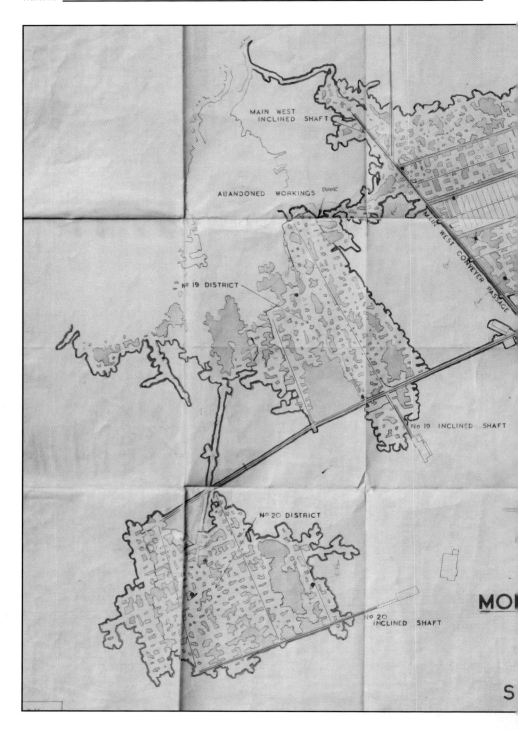

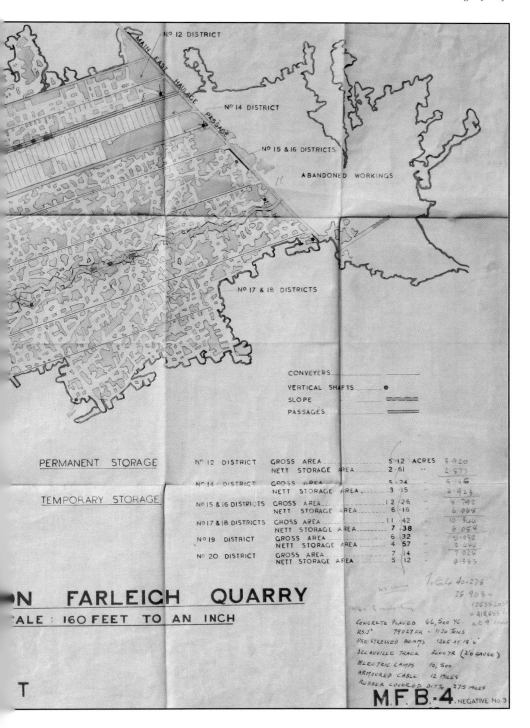

Aerial view of Monkton Farleigh ammunition depot in 1976, after closure and after many of the surface buildings were demolished. Main East entrance is at the top right, Main West to the left and a little above centre, the boilerhouse centre right and the laboratories centre left.

Above: Main West entrance building and its surrounding land in 1990. The laboratory block occupied the ground in front of the copse in the middle background. The land in the foreground was the site of an estate of wooden bungalows occupied by the depot's military police contingent.

Below: Main West entrance seen here in 1985 with restoration almost completed. The prominent 'Prohibited Area' and contraband notices refer to matches, cigarettes or other smoking materials, and metallic objects that might cause a spark, which were all banned from being taken underground. Anyone contravening these regulations would be subject to severe punishment.

Above: Main West was the main entrance for handling all types of ammunition up to the size of 5" howitzer shells, all of which could be carried by the conveyors. Here we see a batch of artillery shells, recently arrived by lorry, being transferred to the main west incline belt to be taken underground for storage.

Below: This photograph, taken in September 1963, shows the last box of ammunition brought from underground at Monkton Farleigh prior to the depot's closure.

Above: Main East entrance building at Monkton Farleigh, a much more lightly constructed building than Main West. Note the concrete top of the inclined shaft descending underground at the end of the building. Main East was fitted with narrow-gauge rails and an overhead rope haulage system and was used primarily for the receipt and issue of heavy calibre armaments.

Below: This is the electric winding engine in Main East building that drove the overhead haulage system.

Above: An ammunition wagon being lowered down Main East shaft by the overhead rope system. On the 'down' side, asbestos-lined skids on the trucks engaged with the raised steel plates seen here between the rails to control the speed of descent. On the 'up' side pivoted steel dogs were fitted to retard trucks that broke away from the haulage rope.

Below: ammunition trucks lined up underground in Main East haulageway.

Above: Main East haulageway in 1985, near the entrance to No.16 District, seen here on the left. Note the star-wheels supporting the overhead haulage rope.

Below: The east end of No.15 District looking out through the blast doors onto Main East haulageway.

Above: The Cathedral-like construction of No.14 District at Monkton Farleigh. It was planned that the entire depot would be constructed to this symmetrical design, but mistakes due to the use of unskilled labour resulted in a serious roof fall and the plan was subsequently abandoned. The storage bays extend some fifty feet out on each side of this passage.

Below: The bottom of No.20 District inclined shaft showing the wooden-framed conveyor. Note the steps on the incline, visible through the open door.

Above: A typical view in No.19 District showing some of the octagonal concrete pillars supporting the roof. The 'U'-shaped concrete blocks on the floor once supported the District conveyor. Notice the neat layout of the conduit on the ceiling for the electric lights. In total there were just over 25,000 lights in the depot.

Below: A bay in No.12 District. From the plan on pages 132-133 it will be seen that a fairly regular layout of pillars was achieved. This was something of a compromise design following the roof collapse in District 14. It was decided, however, that even this design consumed to much time and too many resources, and elsewhere in the depot the original layout of quarry pillars was retained.

Above: The generator hall at Monkton Farleigh, following restoration in 1985/6. Only one Ruston Hornsby VLB5 alternator set was installed here, although the hall was built and fitted out for two units.

Below: The switchroom in Monkton Farleigh's power station. The generator and transformer monitoring panels on the right include one for No.2 generator set, which was never installed.

Above: This was the generator hall at Monkton Farleigh in September 1984, badly vandalised by scrap metal thieves. The generator set is just visible in the background. The generator room and switchroom were restored over the following two years by the author, Bruce Maskery and Mark Rivron.

Below: The floors of many of the main passages were dug up in order to steal the large copper electrical distribution cables buried beneath them. Here we see the author (on the digger) and Sean Williams making a start on clearing up the mess.

Above: The top of the Farleigh Down Tunnel which descended at an inclination of 1 in 8 for a mile and a quarter, linking the underground depot at Monkton Farleigh with Farleigh Down railway sidings on the Bristol to London main line near Box, several hundred feet lower in the valley below.

Below: Because of the length of the tunnel it was necessary to split the Farleigh Down conveyor into two sections; this is the drive motor for the lower conveyor, half way down the tunnel.

Above: At the bottom of the tunnel the conveyor emerged in an underground, narrow-gauge marshalling yard, where the ammunition was transferred onto railway trucks. These were then brought to the surface up a short inclined shaft by means of a Head Wrightson tram creeper.

Below: The tram creeper emerged on the surface in the tin shed seen in the background (which is still extant although in very poor condition). From here the trucks were propelled along a half-mile long raised platform from which transfers were made too and from main line trains.

Above: Between 1984 -1990, during which period this photograph was taken, the Monkton Farleigh depot was open to the public. The tall poles surrounding Main West building are lightning conductors, the ionized air emerging from the underground workings making the building vulnerable to strikes.

Below: The interior of Main West building in 1987, fitted out as a reception area for visitors.

SPRING QUARRY

As we have seen in the introduction to this book, the Fall of France and the consequent advantage to the Luftwaffe in its ability to broaden its range of targets across the United Kingdom precipitated Beaverbrook and the Ministry of Aircraft Production into a panic programme of underground factory construction. This programme was once again focussed, initially at least, upon the Corsham area where vast tracts of readily adaptable underground capacity already existed.

Spring Quarry, together with a number of smaller quarries within a ten-mile radius, was requisitioned by the Ministry of Aircraft Production on 7 December 1940. The 3,300,000 square foot quarry was to be transformed into the largest underground factory in the world, housing the entire engine production line of the Bristol Aeroplane Company, currently located in highly vulnerable surface accommodation at Filton near Bristol. The Filton factory produced the Bristol Hercules radial engine which was the standard power plant for the RAF's bomber force during the early years of the war.

It was confidently expected that the conversion could be completed in six months at a cost of no more than £100,000. The scheme was a disaster in almost every respect. With no prior experience of so complex an engineering project, the government handed control to a prominent firm of civil engineers on a 'costs-plus-profit' basis. In retrospect the costs-plus-profit contract, which was widely used for thousands of wartime government projects, has since been recognized as a licence to print money and an open door for corruption and profiteering. There was probably no worse an example than the Spring Quarry factory where an initial six-month, £100,000 scheme burgeoned into a £13,000,000 fiasco, with construction still unfinished at the end of the war. The factory, which was scheduled to begin production in June 1941 turning out Bristol Hercules engines at the rate of 260 each month, had produced only 523 engines by the time of its closure, most of which were development-stage Centaurus engines that contributed little to the war effort.

By mid-1941, despite a haemorrhage of cash, very little progress had been made at the factory site and BAC, which had at first been very keen to go underground, was exhibiting worrying signs of cold feet. The German bomber threat had dwindled to insignificance and the prospect of operating in a claustrophobic subterranean environment seemed increasingly unappealing. Despite its misgivings, the firm was eventually cajoled into taking up half the space that had been originally allotted to them. Dowty of Gloucester expressed an interest in the partially developed north-west quarter of the quarry but later pulled out, as did the Parnall company of Yate who toyed briefly with the idea of establishing a gun-turret assembly plant in the south-central section of the quarry. Eventually, in early 1943, the south-west area, which had already been partially fitted out for BAC, was occupied by the Birmingham Small Arms Company as a barrel mill making barrels for the Hispano cannon. By the end of 1943 factory development had reached its peak; three-quarters of the quarry was fully occupied and operational and the decision had been taken that no further work would be undertaken in the north-west or 'Dowty' area. The whole concept of the BAC factory had, however, changed. The main Hercules production line was to stay at Filton and, instead, the Spring Quarry site would be used as a development unit for Bristol's new, eighteen-cylinder Centaurus engine.

Despite the fact that the factory was never completed to its full specification the Spring Quarry complex was still an awesome achievement. Personnel access for the 25,000 employees who worked underground was via four high capacity passenger lifts and two Otis escalators, the latter, because new escalators were unobtainable during the war, requisitioned from the London Transport tube stations at Holborn and St. Paul's. Raw materials and finished products were transported by means of four twenty-ton goods lifts and two dedicated machinery lifts – essentially twenty-ton chain hoists suspended above a 100-foot vertical shaft. A separate lift was provided to deliver provisions to the underground kitchens while two others were used solely to remove ash from the underground boiler houses. The ventilation system was prodigious; twenty-one air shafts and fifteen axial flow fans, the largest some fifteen feet in diameter, extracted contaminated air and circulated fresh air, heated by a dozen coal-fired Lancashire boilers housed in two underground boiler houses, via underfloor ducts.

Left: Access to the factory site was controlled by four guard-houses, all of which survived until recent years. The only current survivor is that serving Passenger Lift No.2, situated on Westwells Road, although its future too is in doubt.
The grass-mounded shaft-top building of passenger lift PL2 can be seen to the right of the guardhouse.

Above left: The guardhouse for Machine Lift No.1 Road, demolished in 2012 to make way for the new MoD development on Westwells Road.

Above right: The guardhouse for Goods Lift Access West, on the Bradford Road, demolished in 2001.

Left: The guardhouse for Goods Lift 'C' Road, on the site of the Spring Park development.

Below: Plan showing the extent of Spring quarry and its adjacent workings.

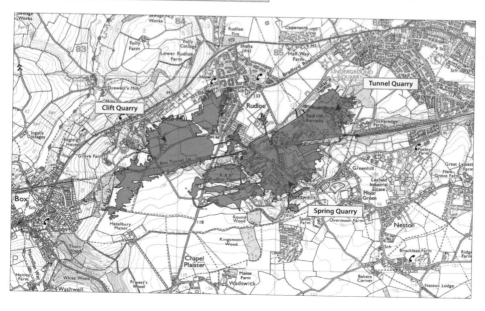

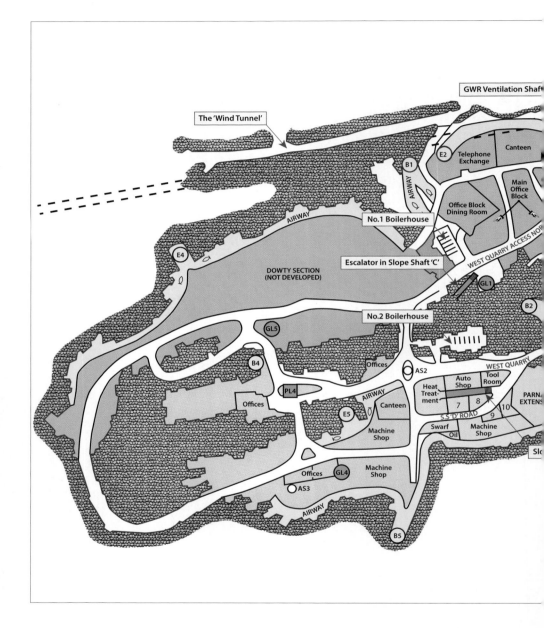

GWR Ventilation Shaft

The 'Wind Tunnel'

Canteen

E2

Telephone
Exchange

B1

AIRWAY

Main
Office
Block

Office Block
Dining Room

No.1 Boilerhouse

AIRWAY

Escalator in Slope Shaft 'C'

WEST QUARRY ACCESS NOR

E4

DOWTY SECTION
(NOT DEVELOPED)

GL1

No.2 Boilerhouse

B2

GL5

B4

Offices

AS2

WEST QUARRY

Auto
Shop

Tool
Room

Heat
Treat-
ment

PL4

7

8

10

PARN
EXTENS

Offices

AIRWAY

E5

Canteen

S.S 'D' ROAD

9

Swarf

Machine
Shop

Machine
Shop

Oil

Slc

Offices

GL4

Machine
Shop

AS3

AIRWAY

B5

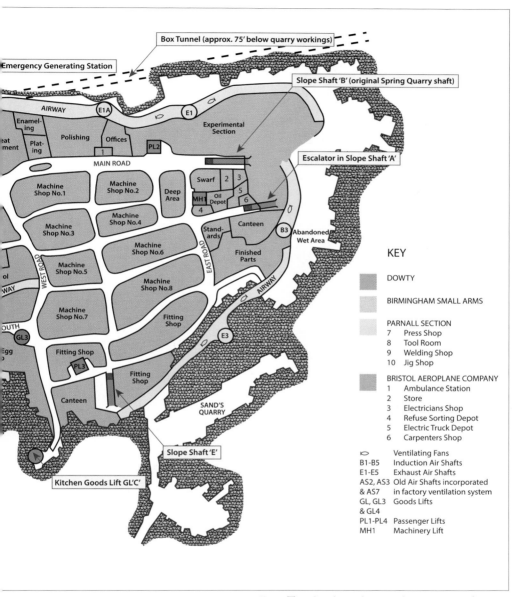

Box Tunnel (approx. 75' below quarry workings)

Emergency Generating Station

Slope Shaft 'B' (original Spring Quarry shaft)

AIRWAY · E1A · E1

Enamel-ing · Polishing · Plating · Offices · PL2 · eat ment · Plat-ing

Experimental Section

MAIN ROAD

Escalator in Slope Shaft 'A'

Machine Shop No.1 · Machine Shop No.2 · Deep Area · Swarf · 2 · 3 · MH1 · Oil Depot · 5 · 4 · 6

Machine Shop No.4 · Canteen

Machine Shop No.3 · Stand-ards · B3 · Abandoned Wet Area

Machine Shop No.6 · Finished Parts

Machine Shop No.5

Machine Shop No.8 · AIRWAY

Machine Shop No.7 · Fitting Shop · E3

WEST ROAD · EAST ROAD

SOUTH · GL3 · Egg

Fitting Shop · PL3

Fitting Shop

Canteen · SAND'S QUARRY

Slope Shaft 'E'

Kitchen Goods Lift GL'C'

KEY

DOWTY

BIRMINGHAM SMALL ARMS

PARNALL SECTION
7   Press Shop
8   Tool Room
9   Welding Shop
10   Jig Shop

BRISTOL AEROPLANE COMPANY
1   Ambulance Station
2   Store
3   Electricians Shop
4   Refuse Sorting Depot
5   Electric Truck Depot
6   Carpenters Shop

    Ventilating Fans
B1-B5   Induction Air Shafts
E1-E5   Exhaust Air Shafts
AS2, AS3   Old Air Shafts incorporated
& AS7   in factory ventilation system
GL, GL3   Goods Lifts
& GL4
PL1-PL4   Passenger Lifts
MH1   Machinery Lift

Above: This plan shows the general arrangement of workshops and other facilities within the group of underground factories constructed in Spring quarry.

Left: Very few photographs have been discovered of the Spring quarry factory in operation.

Here we see cylinder head components and part of the valve gear for a Bristol Centaurus engine being assembled. Many of the early engines built in the underground factory failed under test, the faults being attributed primarily to the unsatisfactory working conditions in the factory.

Note the early use of fluorescent lighting seen in this image.

Right: A view through a window and a study in concentration.... is it an engineering problem they are trying to resolve, or maybe they are concerned that a production schedule is not being met...

Left: Although the original photograph was not captioned, it is probable that this image, in the Centaurus development factory, shows a toolmaker at work. Note once again the fluorescent lighting. One of the many shortcomings of the Spring quarry factory was that because of the random distribution of support pillars and the varying roof heights it was difficult to achieve an adequate overall level of light in the workshops, so very large numbers of individual machine lights were required.

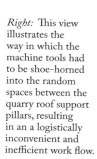

Right: This view illustrates the way in which the machine tools had to be shoe-horned into the random spaces between the quarry roof support pillars, resulting in an a logistically inconvenient and inefficient work flow.

Above & below: surface and underground views of Emergency Adit 'E', from the main underground operatives canteen. This shaft surfaced behind the Stephens plastic factory beside the road that now goes to Wadswick Green. The shaft was blocked-up in the mid-1980s as a security measure.

Above: The massively engineered shaft-head building above goods lift GL3.

Below: The lower landing of passenger lift PL1, still very much in its wartime condition. The lift surfaces in the prominent, earth-mounded structure on the west side of Westwells Road, illustrated on page 194.

Above: Another Corsham concrete monolith: this the shaft head building for passenger lift PL4.
Below: Rather different in design to all the other Spring quarry lift-head buildings, this is the structure at the head of goods lift GL2 and Machinery Lift ML2.

Above: The twenty-ton travelling crane suspended above machinery lift shaft ML2

Above right: The lift cage for goods lift GL4 with its associated five-ton overhead crane.

Right: An early wartime view looking up the shaft off Machinery Lift ML1. This shows a packing case containing machine tool components for the Bristol Aeroplane Company's engine factory being delivered underground.

Above: The surface structure above the west escalator shaft, modified in the 1950s for its Cold War role.

Below: Neither of the escalators requisitioned for use at Corsham were the correct length for the shafts, so in the west shaft, where the unit from Holborn station was fitted, the main escalator was terminated in a sub-ground chamber with a short auxiliary escalator to the surface.

Above: Viewed in the opposite direction from the image below left, this photograph shows the top of the long escalator descending into the factory.

Below: The lower landing of the west escalator. There is an inclined wagon runway on the far side of the left hand wall.

Above: The lower landing of one of the lifts at the east end of the factory, in a section of the site used in later years by the Admiralty for general storage.

Below: a corner of the factory that in later days served as a vehicle maintenance section of the Central Government Emergency War Headquarters. This photograph illustrates how some areas of the quarry had very sound ceiling strata allowing broad, open areas unobstructed by roof supports. Note the corrugated asbestos sheet on the right, put up to drain away seepage water from the roof.

Above: A typical junction in the roadways that served the workshops of the former Bristol Aeroplane engine factory in Spring quarry.

Below: When the underground factory closed soon after the war, a large part of it was put over to Admiralty storage while about half of the east end of the quarry was reconstructed as the Central Government Emergency War Headquarters. Between the two areas a security buffer zone or 'dead area' was established. In that area all the factory fixtures and fittings were removed but the brick shells of the workshops and offices, etc. remain.

Above: Empty concrete plinths which once supported machine tools in the 'dead area' of Spring quarry.

Below: This view shows a minor roadway between workshops in the 'dead area'. To aid ventilation most of the walls of the workshop areas were filled with wire mesh in wooden frames rather than built of solid brickwork. The perforated brick wall on the right is part of a ventilation extraction duct.

Above: Something from the more recent past: this worker's smoking bay was in a section of Spring quarry used for Admiralty storage until 1995.

Below: Parts issuing hatches in what was the factory's jig and tool store.

Above: External view of one of the large ventilation input fans. The units drew air from the surface down a vertical shaft, distributing it around the factory via under-floor ducts.

Below: This is a 'butterfly' valve in one of the main under-floor ventilation ducts. It could be closed remotely from the factory ARP centre to prevent circulation in the event of a warning of gas attack.

Above: A junction in the system of ventilation ducts beneath the factory floor. The figure in this photograph gives some idea of the scale of these ducts.

Below: Taken during its demolition, this photograph shows the massive, bomb-proof surface structure of the 'Queen Mary' shaft which supplied air to a 20-foot diameter fan capable of moving 500,000 cubic feet of air per minute, removing dust and fumes from the factory's heat treatment plant.

Spring Quarry

165

Above: This is No.2 underground boilerhouse at Spring quarry, one of two boilerhouses, each fitted out in 1941 with six secondhand boilers supplied by Hopkins of Huddersfield. No.2 boilerhouse was originally provided with an overhead-belt coal feed system and Crossthwaite mechanical stokers, but these were so badly set up that they were quickly abandoned and hand-firing resorted to. Jointly, the boilers consumed 487 tons of coal per week.

Left: A more detailed view of one of the Hopkins boilers in No.2 boilerhouse. Soon after the war, when much of the quarry was taken over by the Admiralty for storage, the boilers were converted to oil-firing, the apparatus for which can be seen at the front of the fire tubes.
In the early 1970s both underground boilerhouses were decommissioned and replaced by a new installation on the surface, seen opposite.

Above: The new, 1970s boilerhouse can be seen in the top centre of this photograph. The distinctive quatrefoil chimney stack was a prominent feature of the Corsham skyline for many years. Below the boilerhouse can be seen the shaft-head buildings for lifts PL4 and GL2.

Below: An interior view of the surface boilerhouse at Spring quarry, shortly after it was decommissioned.

Above: The emergency generator set in Spring quarry, installed post-war when the Admiralty took possession of the quarry. Although quite a large plant, this unit could do little more than maintain power to the emergency lighting system in the event of a mains failure.

Below: The Bristol Aeroplane Co's factory was provided with sufficient toilets for the use of its workforce of 25,000 personnel, and this required a very large underground sewage disposal plant. The compressors seen here provided power for the pneumatic ejectors which pumped this sewage to the surface.

OLGA LEHMANN'S MURALS

Distressed by the dull colour schemes suggested by the Ministry of Works for the underground canteens at Spring Quarry, Sir Reginald Verdon Smith, Chairman of the Bristol Aeroplane Company, invited Olga Lehmann, a talented young film set designer, to decorate the canteens with brightly coloured floor-to-ceiling murals. The hope was that a more cheerful environment would raise the morale and brighten the spirits of the workforce.

Many years later, Olga Lehmann explained the background to her work: ' Each canteen took about a week to a fortnight to complete and management provided the materials – oil paint and solvents. The first impression of the factory made quite an impact, reminding me of the film *'Metropolis'*. It was lit by what appeared to be bright daylight, which was in fact neon strip lighting the likes of which I had never seen before'.

Each of the eight canteens was decorated to a different theme, including horse racing, gambling, American circus, Follie Bergere, prehistoric animals etc. Many of the murals have survived but some have been lost, painted over when the Admiralty took control of the site. Immediately after Olga Lehmann's work was completed, Verdon Smith commissioned a black & white photographic record of the murals, two of which are reproduced here.

Right: The canteen decorated with a horse racing theme.

Below: A corner of the circus themed canteen; unfortunately these murals are now lost.

This page & opposite: Surviving murals in the horse racing themed canteen adjacent to the main office block at the north end of the factory. In later years this area was adapted as a dormitory for an RAF underground Cold War control centre, hence the bunks visible in some of the photographs.

Above & below: These two murals are part of a series illustrating the pleasures of over-indulgence: food, drink and gambling.

Above: Riddled with political incorrectness in today's world, this mural depicts a Church of England clergyman being boiled alive by cannibals. It is believed that this image was created by Olga Lehmann's assistant, Gilbert Wood and is a dark reference to his abuse in childhood.

Below: A bar at the Follie Bergere (spoiled by the vent holes cut in the wall and subsequently bricked up).

Above & below: 'Prehistoric animal' murals in the large operatives canteen at the far east end of the factory, at the base of Escalator Shaft 'A'. The majority of the paintings in this area were the joint work of Olga Lehmann and Gilbert Wood. This canteen area was also provided with a stage and other facilities for the mounting of entertainments by ENSA and similar organisations.

Above: The stage in the 'prehistoric animals' canteen. Many famous entertainers performed here, including Dame Myra Hess, who gave a piano recital on a baby grand, brought down especially for the event.

Below: The ticket booth where workers bought tickets for the entertainments.

Above: A montage of horses' heads, one of the more striking and surreal of Olga Lehmann's murals.

Below: While decorating the canteens, Olga Lehmann took time to paint a small number of watercolours recording her impressions of the factory. Here we see what appears to be a large press-brake in the centre of the image with a milling machine in the background and a pile of engine cowlings to the left.

RNSD COPENACRE

Above: Aerial view of the above-ground complex at RNSD Copenacre towards the end of its active life.

Below: Schematic layout of the underground stores at Copenacre, taken from the depot's fire escape plan.

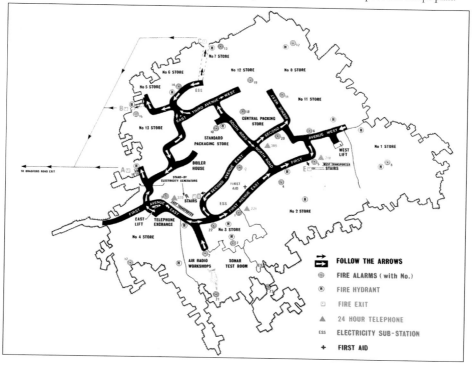

Above & below: Two views of the massive concrete shaft-head building for the east transporter at Copenacre. The winding engine for the transporter in the inclined shaft is in the concrete structure while the lorry loading bays are beneath the asbestos roof to the right. It was calculated that this building would be so difficult and expensive to demolish that it was left in place when the site was redeveloped for housing.

Above: Inside the east transporter shaft building, looking down into the depot. The transporter rails are in the middle of the image, loading bay gates on the right and the top of the pedestrian steps on the left.
Below: The base of the transporter shaft looking up, with the transporter platform in the foreground.

Above: Sunk below the level of the surrounding land, the monolithic west transporter building was hardly visible from the A4 trunk road, just yards away.

Below: The surrealy sinister shaft top building for the west goods and passenger lift. The weather vane propped beside the loading bay once stood on top of the concrete structure, adding to the air of menace.

Above: The lower lift landing of the west lift. Note the fire exit map beside the emergency exit door.

Below: First Avenue East (see map on p.177), a typical roadway through the storage areas.

Above: The junction of North Road and Second Avenue.

Below: The entrance to No.4 Store, which, according to the sign on the gate held gauges and Lynx helicopter parts, amongst other items.

Above: The underground boilerhouse. These modern, oil-fired units replaced four Cochran boilers installed in 1942. The Cochrans were lowered into the quarry via the large shaft on the far side of the road opposite the main gates to the surface loading platforms and offices.

Below: Naval electronic gear underwent numerous tests while in store; the motor-generator sets and other equipment seen here produced current at the required voltages and frequencies for these tests.

Above & below: Miscellaneous Naval stores stacked in the depot when at the peak of its operational life.

Above & below: Power supplies, test equipment and equipment under test in the underground laboratory.

Above & below: Two more views of RNSD Copenacre in its operational days. The yellow electric trucks were ubiquitous throughout the government owned quarries at Corsham.

CLUBHOUSE QUARRY

Soon after the Second World War drew to a close, rumours began to circulate that vast sums of foreign currency were hidden in a secret quarry beneath Corsham. Attention slowly focussed on Clubhouse quarry in Neston, but by the 1960s, when interest in the missing hoard intensified, no trace of the quarry could be found and it was assumed that the land that its entrance shaft occupied had been built over. It was further rumoured that the quarry had flooded and all the stored banknotes had been destroyed. The problem was that the wartime plans had been extraordinarily secret and no documentation, at that time, was in the public domain, so everything that was known was word-of-mouth and highly speculative.

Then, in the 1980s, the late David Pollard unearthed a lease from the Bath Stone Firms that indicated that the De La Rue Company had indeed taken possession of Clubhouse quarry for undisclosed storage purposes. De La Rue are high security document, cheque and currency-note printers, so obvious conclusions were drawn. The location of the quarry, however, had still not been discovered.

In 2013 the author of this book discovered in the archives of the De La Rue Company, which had only recently been made available for inspection, that the company had taken possession of Clubhouse quarry to store huge quantities of banknotes it had printed for a number of East European countries but which it could not deliver because those countries had been over-run by the German army. Further, its works in Bunhill Road, Basingstoke had been destroyed by bombing in September 1940 and it was in desperate need of alternative accommodation.

The following year, 2014, the author and Bruce Maskery made a thorough search of the Neston area, and in the back garden of a house in Neston Crescent a structure that had to be a ventilation shaft for Clubhouse quarry was discovered. A rapid negotiation with the householder, and the help of two younger and fitter accomplices, Bradley Wyatt and Paul Hurren, resulted in access being gained and the photographs that follow being taken...

Below: The Clubhouse quarry ventilation shaft. Seventy years worth of garden waste had to be cleared from the shaft and a grid of iron security bars cut away before access was possible.

Above: A panoramic view of almost the whole of Clubhouse quarry. The vertical ventilation shaft is just out of shot on the left. The original inclined access shaft is on the far right. This is completely blocked at the top, and a house in Fleetwood Close is built over it.

Below: It was discovered that only a small part of the quarry had flooded, due to seepage from the air-shaft. Disconcertingly, the bottom of the shaft terminated in a large iron tank bolted to the ceiling, from which, when the quarry was in use, the seepage water was pumped to a surface drainage system.

Below: Ventilation air was drawn from the shaft via the duct, seen here, which emerged from the tank above water level. By the time this photo was taken all the air ducting had been removed.

Below: having climbed down the 80-foot shaft, and finishing up in a tank full of water, it was necessary to crawl out of the air duct to gain access to the quarry.

Above: The currency repository was divided up into four separate chambers, each secured by a massive Chubb vault door, all of which, like the one seen here, are still in place.

Below: A view up the main access shaft to Clubhouse quarry. At the top, a security door has been jammed shut, the space behind filled with rubble and the foundations of the house in Fleetwood Close built on top.

SECTION 4

BURLINGTON

As the Second World War drew to a close, the Spring quarry factory became increasingly irrelevant. From the very start of the venture the Bristol Aeroplane Company had been reluctant to take up residence, and by the time they took full occupancy the threat to their conventional factories from the Luftwaffe had diminished to negligible proportions. Meanwhile, at the Treasury, there were serious misgivings about the vast sums of money that had been squandered on the project. However, by 1946 developments in the world's balance of military and political power presented the government with some justification for the expense of the Corsham project. Russia had developed the atom bomb and, to the somewhat paranoid security services, seemed bent upon world domination. It was thought that in the event of an atomic war with Soviet Russia, London would be a prime target and that if the necessary steps were not taken, the first bomb would wipe out the seat of government, the nation and the Empire would descend into rudderless, lawless anarchy and it would be the end of the world as we knew it. The assumption was that the preservation of Britain as a democratic, civilised entity, would depend upon the continuity of government and to secure that end a secure, bomb-proof and radiation-proof bolt-hole for central government must be found.

As early as 1946 Eric de Normann of the Ministry of Works, when questioned about the post-war disposal of the Spring quarry factory, replied *'the policy is to hold on firmly to our best refuge from the atomic bomb'*. Nothing was done immediately, and the policy remained to keep the seat of government in wartime in London, but by the Spring of 1951 a top secret cabinet committee reported that, in the aftermath of a Soviet attack:

'London might become completely isolated and out of touch with the rest of the country; and in that event there would be no object in keeping the central machinery of government underground in London. We are therefore beginning also to consider the possibility of providing some alternative seat of government in another part of the country and equipping it in advance with the necessary accommodation and communications.'

Following upon this a series of further cabinet committees considered the problem and eventually, in September 1955, the Prime Minister authorised the conversion of a large part of the east end of Spring quarry into the Central Government Emergency War Headquarters, initially code-named *Subterfuge*. The detailed story of the development of this project is too long to be told here, but can be found in Nick Catford's seminal work on the scheme *'Burlington'* published by Folly Books. In July 1956 a contract for the main infrastructure work was issued to the Devizes based building firm of Chivers & Co., and a year later it was reported that the job was 65% complete. Development was held-up by delays in the delivery of some important air-conditioning plant from Sulzers, which was not available until the winter of 1961. Eventually, in the summer of 1963, the Prime Minister was told that the bunker, earlier re-named *Stockwell* and now, since August 1961 known as *Burlington* was at last ready for use.

Throughout this period, there had been much confusion over exactly what the role of the Corsham bunker should be: would it be operational during the period of heightened international tension in the lead-up to nuclear war? Should it be the site to which the central government decamps at the moment war becomes inevitable? Or should it be the location from which the recovery from war should be administered? These questions were raised as construction progressed in a series of Cabinet minutes. Early in 1961 it was recorded:

As you know, Stockwell is intended primarily as a battle headquarters for the higher direction of the country's administration during the attack and survival periods, and planning to date has been based on this concept. However, on 3 February 1961 the Machinery of Government Sub-Committee agreed that it was desirable to consider what functions Stockwell might exercise in the precautionary period before attack. The extent to which the headquarters could take on responsibilities at such a time may affect organisational arrangements in Whitehall and elsewhere. It may also be relevant to the phasing of plans for the manning of Stockwell in an emergency; though in view of the importance of ensuring continuance of government control the exercise of functions in the precautionary period could not be allowed to hinder the manning of Stockwell very early in the precautionary period if Ministers so ordered.

By August 1961 there was, however, a change of tack:

The central nucleus of government will remain in London throughout the precautionary period, the function of Burlington will be to act as the seat of government in the period of survival and reconstruction so that while, therefore, the staffs at Burlington will need to be kept currently informed from Whitehall of the progress of war preparatory matter (so that they can take over smoothly when and if necessary) no substantive functions will be exercised from Burlington during the precautionary stage.'

Only two months later yet another scheme was proposed:

Burlington would act as the ultimate source of authority during the period of survival and reconstruction, and be an alternative centre to London for authorising Nuclear Retaliation. It is assumed that the Prime Minister would take on the responsibility for defence and that the War Cabinet would consist of a small number of senior Ministers with other Ministers and Chiefs of Staff attending meetings as required. The Chiefs of Defence Staff would be housed in the War Cabinet Organisation area, but other Chiefs of Staff would be elsewhere in the headquarters.

The fact was that no sooner was construction of the bunker under way than serious doubts were raised concerning the overall viability of the site, some members of the Machinery of Government in War Sub-Committee voicing the opinion that, essentially, they had lumbered themselves with a white-elephant that could not be kept secret, that did not offer sufficient protection from nuclear weapons and that, giving the planning assumptions that led to its construction, could not, with any degree of reliability, be adequately manned in order to perform its required functions. The problem was that although it was located more than one hundred miles from London and was deep underground, it was neither deep enough nor sufficiently well protected to withstand the effects of even a near miss from a nuclear weapon. The committee's response was to minute that:

'since security is vital for Turnstile, [yet another code-name for the Corsham bunker] *(or any plan that succeeds it – other than a genuinely invulnerable redoubt), it becomes imperative to take a decision about its future.'*

Possible alternative courses of action to follow included:

'the concept of adopting a completely different type of organisation that would be based from the start on dispersal, and even mobility.'

Having invested so heavily in the Corsham project, however, the committee was loath to discard it completely and recommended in May 1963 that:

'under any alternative plan something would still remain at Turnstile because it is too valuable an installation to abandon entirely. One point for examination will be the extent to which it might still be possible to preserve Turnstile, for as long as we can, as a cover story for the new plan. This in itself will be helped if we can keep it in the plan but as something other than the potential central seat of government.'

It would appear that the plan of establishing a number of smaller, dispersed and mobile cells, later referred to as *'Python Groups'* in place of one static hardened government facility was adopted, and by the mid-1960s the Corsham site was pretty well redundant. Although there were recurrent plans to re-activate the site, including a scheme from the mid-1980s known as *Project Albatross,* which would have seen about half the site refurbished to house a staff of no more than 1,000 personnel, little or nothing was done to progress these schemes and, as will be seen from the photographs which follow, the bunker today is much as it was in 1963.

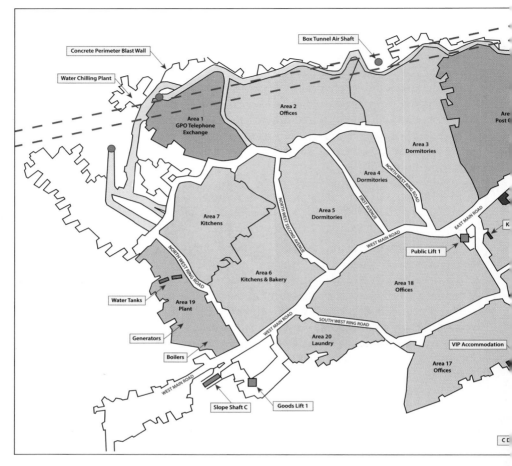

Concrete Perimeter Blast Wall

Water Chilling Plant

Box Tunnel Air Shaft

Area 1
GPO Telephone
Exchange

Area 2
Offices

Area 3
Dormitories

Area 4
Dormitories

Area 5
Dormitories

Area 7
Kitchens

Area 6
Kitchens & Bakery

Public Lift 1

Area 18
Offices

Water Tanks

Area 19
Plant

Generators

Boilers

Area 20
Laundry

VIP Accommodation

Area 17
Offices

Slope Shaft C

Goods Lift 1

NORTH WEST RING ROAD

NORTH WEST SECOND AVENUE

FIRST AVENUE

WEST MAIN ROAD

EAST MAIN ROAD

SOUTH WEST RING ROAD

WEST MAIN ROAD

WEST MAIN ROAD

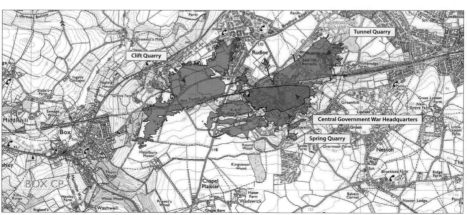

Tunnel Quarry

Clift Quarry

Rudloe

Central Government War Headquarters

Spring Quarry

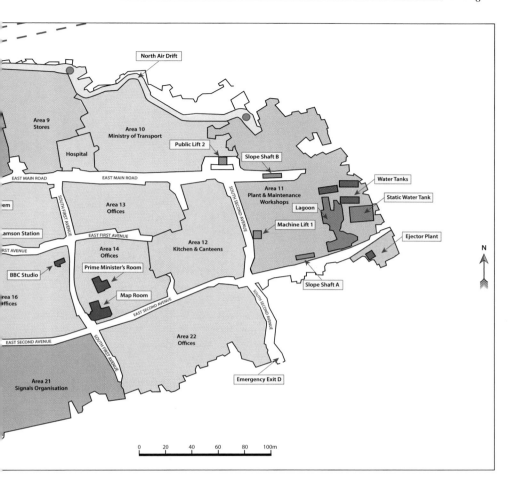

Above: Between 1957 and 1963 the upper section of the east end of the former Bristol Aeroplane Company's underground factory at Spring quarry was converted into the Central Government Emergency War Headquarters. The general layout of the quarry's roadways,etc. was retained and each of the large workshop areas, amounting to approximately five acres each in extent, became either suites of offices for various government departments, dormitories or service areas. Each section was given an 'Area' number,from 1 to 22, as shown on the plan above.

Opposite: Plan showing the position of the government bunker within the former factory complex, superimposed upon a surface map.

KEY TO GOVERNMENT OFFICES

Area 2
Board of Trade
Customs & Excise
Lord Chancellor's Office
Ministry of Pensions & National Insurance
Office of Minister for Science
Stationery Office
Treasury
Ministry of Works

Area 13
Ministry of Agriculture, Fisheries & Food
Ministry of Power

Area 14
War Cabinet
Ministry of Defence
Joint Intelligence Committee

Area 15
Camp Commandant
Establishment Officers Branch

Area 16
BBC Studio
Central Office of Information
Ministry of Health
Home Office
Ministry of Housing
& Local Government
Scottish Office
United Kingdom Land Forces

Area 17
Ministry of Aviation
Ministry of Labour

Area 18
Admiralty
Air Ministry
War Office

Area 22
Colonial Office
Foreign & Commonwealth Office

Above: the shaft-head building for passenger lift PL1, rebuilt and earth-mounded to serve as one of the main entrances to the Burlington bunker.

Below: Inside the shaft-head building, two sets of steel blast doors, seen on the left, give access to an air-lock protecting the lift shaft.

Right: A view through the shaft-top air-lock with the lift cage doors visible in the distance.

Below: The interior of the lift cage with its doors open on the upper landing. The open doors of the air-lock can be seen in the background. Although the lighting, and probably the floor panels, of the lift have been modernised, the wood panelling seems to be of original wartime vintage, as is the rotary Otis lift controller on the left hand wall.

PLEASE KEEP CLEAR OF LIFT GATES

Above: Passenger lift No.1 on the lower landing in the Burlington bunker.

Below: Just around the corner from the lift one is on East Main Road, from which branch numerous subsidiary roads accessing various government departments.

Above: The Ministry of Transport map room, from where shipping and all forms of inland transport would be co-ordinated following a nuclear attack on Britain.

Below: A typical, somewhat Spartan, senior Civil Servant's combined office and bedroom in the Ministry of Transport section of the headquarters.

Area 8: The Telephone Exchange and G.P.O Services

Above: A detailed plan of Area 8, the G.P.O (General Post Office) telephone services section of the bunker. This area contained not only the bunker's internal, external and international telephone exchange, but also a full suite of offices for all the various functions carried out by the Post Office Telephone Service nation wide. The key to the various offices shown opposite gives some idea of the range of functions, some of which would be patently irrelevant in event of a nuclear war, for which provision was made. Those functions irrelevant in wartime would, of course, come into their own during the period of post-war recovery and reconstruction.

KEY TO AREA 8

GENERAL DIRECTORATE
26 Director-General
24 Private Secretary
23 Liaison Officer

ENGINEERING DEPARTMENT
21 Deputy Engineer-in-Chief
22 Private Secretary
17 Engineering Officer
19 Engineering Officer
Main Lines: Development, Maintenance, Planning
& Provision
52 Officer-in-Charge
53 Deputy
Circuit Provision Group
54 Officer-in-Charge, Public circuits, BBC, AM, USAF, ROC,
    HO, MOT, MOA
55 CEGB, Nationalised Undertakings, Public Utilities, Press
    Admiralty, WO, FO, GCHQ, DTN, PO Admin
    Circuit Advice Control, card records, line plant records etc
Telecommunications Services Intelligence
51 Officer-in-Charge
Lines Information Group (Fault Control)
56 Officer-in-Charge
Emergency Equipment Group
56 Officer-in-Charge
Emergency Equipment Group
56 Officer-in-Charge
55 Typing
51 Drawing Office
Power Branch
57 Officer-in-Charge
Radio Planning & Provision Branch (WI & WO)
50 Officer-in-Charge
49 Radio above 30 mc/s
54 Radio below 30 mc/s
Submarine Branch (Sub)
58 Officer-in-Charge. Laying & Maintenance Operations
56 Submarine Cables. Depot Maintenance
    & Cable Stocks
Subs. Apparatus & Misc. Branch (S) Telephone Exchange
Systems & Trunk Switching (E, TPD & TPM)
44 Officer-in-Charge
43 Deputy
45 Subscribers' Apparatus & Miscellaneous & Telephone
    Exchange Systems & Trunk Switching Group
Telegraph Branch
42 Officer-in-Charge
45 General Questions
Provision of Telegraph Circuits & Equipment for:
45 Air Ministry, Admiralty, Foreign Office, GCHQ,
    War Office & Other Users
Additional Suite
63, 64, 65

POSTAL SERVICES DEPARTMENT
18 Director
16 Chief Inspector
33 Principal (Home Mails) & Senior Inspector (Home Mails)
34 Principal (Overseas Mails)
    & Senior Inspector (Overseas Mails)
35 Principal (General Assistance on Postal Matters)

INLAND TELECOMMUNICATIONS
27 Director
25 Assistant Secretary
20 Principal
Services Group
Provision of Service
59 Officer-in-Charge
60 General Questions & Air Ministry, Ministry of Aviation
61 Admiralty, Foreign Office, GCHQ, GCB,
    MOD, Home Office, War Office, UKLF
Priorities
46 Priorities
Circuit Utilisation Control
39 Officer-in-Charge
41A Circuit Utilisation Control
Telephone Service
Operating & Routing
40 Officer-in-Charge
41 Operating & Routing
Equipment Plans
47 Equipment Plans
Telegraph Service
48 Plans
59A Liaison Duty

RADIO SERVICES DEPARTMENT
12 Director
11 Assistant Secretary
Radio & Broadcasting Services
7   Officer-in-Charge
2   Frequency Plans above 30 mc/s
4   Frequency Plans below 30 mc/s
6   Wireless Telegraph Ship-to-Shore Communications
8   Inspector of Wireless Telegraphy
9   Accountant-General's Department

EXTERNAL TELECOMMUNICATIONS EXECUTIVE
Engineering
13 Director
14 Deputy Director
38 Officer-in-Charge
36 Telegraphs
37 Radio
31 Lines & Telephones
Traffic
32 Telephones & Telegraphs

COMMON SERVICES
1,28 Messengers
29,30 Registry
62 Typists (Teleprinter Room)

UNALLOCATED
5, 10, 15

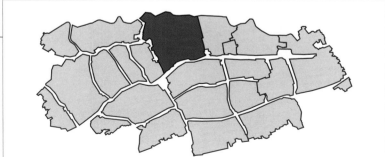

Above: The main switchboard, showing the 40-position inland exchange on the left and the 14-position international exchange on the right.

Left: A closer view of the international exchange console.

Above: A wider view of the underground telephone exchange in Burlington. The Supervisor's desk is in the centre foreground with the Directory Enquiries desk to the left.

Below: The distribution frame and relay racks, etc. in the exchange repeater station.

Above: Channel carrier equipment and repeater racks in the exchange transmission section.

Below: A motor-generator set in the telephone exchange power room.

KEY TO AREA 12

- DINING AREA
- KITCHEN
- SERVERIES
- LAUNDRY
- FEMALE WC
- MALE WC
- SHOWERS
- PLANT
- STORES

EAST MAIN ROAD

MALE WCS
FEMALE WCS
SHOWERS
SUB STN
LAUNDRY
T15
T16
SOUTH SECOND AVENUE
T10
SERVERY
KITCHEN
T12
T13
T14
EAST FIRST AVENUE
COFFEE BAR
T24
FOOD STORAGE
T30
T23
T29
SUB STN
TEMPORARY STORES
T28
DISH-WASHING
T27
DINING AREA
T31
ENGINEERS' STORES
EAST SECOND AVENUE

Area 12 - The East Kitchen

This area, adjacent to the Prime Minister's map room and offices and the conference rooms of the War Cabinet, served the senior members of staff in the Emergency War Headquarters. This area remains in surprisingly good condition but a similar cooking and catering facility at the west end of the bunker, provided for more junior staff, has fallen into decay.

205

Above & below: The East servery, constructed in a particularly deep area of the quarry. The servery, with its bain marie counters and the kitchens (behind the curtain walls to the left of the upper picture) are approached via flights of steps and inclined walkways from the dining rooms above.

Above: The senior officials' coffee bar, complete with stylish Italian coffee machines.

Below: A small corner of the east kitchen, fitted out with large-scale industrial catering equipment.

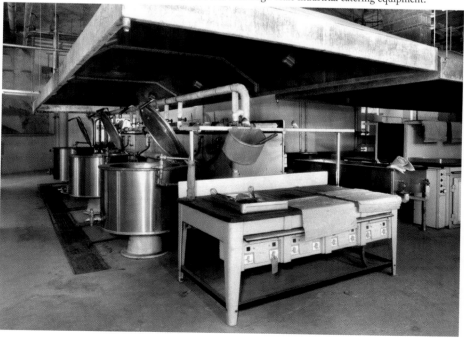

Above: More industrial catering equipment in the east kitchen.
Below: a section of the senior officers' dining room with the coffee bar in the background.

Above: A 1960s vintage dishwashing machine in the preparation area of the east kitchen.

Below: Laundry equipment (with a blanket-press in the background), in the east kitchen area. There was a fully fitted laundry in Area 20, but it would appear that the machines seen here were moved to the east catering section during the abortive preparations for *Operation Albatross* in the 1980s.

Above: Situated in Area 6, adjacent to the now derelict west kitchens, is the bakery, complete with this magnificent 'Mason' fully automatic bread making machine, capable of making 1,000 4lb per eight-hour shifts. Installation, at a cost of £2,096, was completed in October 1958.

Below: The bakery bread ovens, powered by the same diesel fuel used by the bunker's standby generators.

Above: The derelict remains of the west kitchen. The whole western end of the Emergency Government Headquarters appears to have been abandoned at an early stage, possibly as early as 1965. Some of the catering equipment from here seems to have been transferred in the 1980s to the nearby underground RAF Operations Centre.

Below: One of the partially stripped-out serveries in the west kitchen and dining area.

Above: A view in Area 9, the stores section of the bunker with racks of assorted janitorial supplies.

Below: Assorted catering equipment in the stores.

Above: With Armageddon on the horizon, the Civil Service obviously thought some little luxuries were still essential: a butter-pat making machine in the bunker's catering store.

Below: Some of the 2000 waste paper bins, still wrapped in brown paper since the early 1960s, in the stores waiting to be distributed to their designated offices.

213

Above: A tiny part of the bunker's stock of typing paper and other stationery stores. The designation 'R2/21' on the packages marked with red triangles indicates that they are destined for Room 2 in Area 21.

Below: Nothing seems to have been forgotten: staples, balls of string, and probably sealing wax too (although I can't actually see any in this photograph).

Area 14 - The War Cabinet Section

This area, at the east end of the bunker and in close proximity to the government communication centre, was the heart of the bunker where all key strategic decisions would be made. The area included the War Cabinet accommodation, the Prime Minister's map room and the Prime Minister's living quarters.

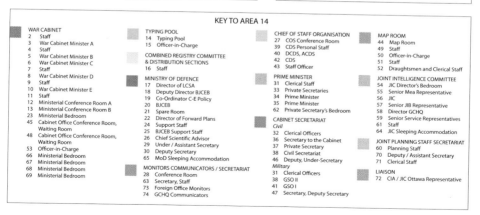

KEY TO AREA 14

WAR CABINET
2 Staff
3 War Cabinet Minister A
4 Staff
5 War Cabinet Minister B
6 War Cabinet Minister C
7 Staff
8 War Cabinet Minister D
9 Staff
10 War Cabinet Minister E
11 Staff
12 Ministerial Conference Room A
13 Ministerial Conference Room B
23 Ministerial Bedroom
45 Cabinet Office Conference Room, Waiting Room
48 Cabinet Office Conference Room, Waiting Room
53 Officer-in-Charge
66 Ministerial Bedroom
67 Ministerial Bedroom
68 Ministerial Bedroom
69 Ministerial Bedroom

TYPING POOL
14 Typing Pool
15 Officer-in-Charge

COMBINED REGISTRY COMMITTEE & DISTRIBUTION SECTIONS
16 Staff

MINISTRY OF DEFENCE
17 Director of LCSA
18 Deputy Director BJCEB
19 Co-Ordinator C-E Policy
20 BJCEB
21 Spare Room
22 Director of Forward Plans
24 Support Staff
25 BJCEB Support Staff
26 Chief Scientific Advisor
29 Under / Assistant Secretary
30 Deputy Secretary
65 MoD Sleeping Accommodation

MONITORS COMMUNICATORS / SECRETARIAT
28 Conference Room
63 Secretary, Staff
73 Foreign Office Monitors
74 GCHQ Communicators

CHIEF OF STAFF ORGANISATION
27 COS Conference Room
39 CDS Personal Staff
40 DCDS, ACDS
42 CDS
43 Staff Officer

PRIME MINISTER
31 Clerical Staff
33 Private Secretaries
34 Prime Minister
35 Prime Minister
62 Private Secretary's Bedroom

CABINET SECRETARIAT
Civil
32 Clerical Officers
36 Secretary to the Cabinet
37 Private Secretary
38 Civil Secretariat
46 Deputy, Under-Secretary
Military
31 Clerical Officers
38 GSO II
41 GSO I
47 Secretary, Deputy Secretary

MAP ROOM
44 Map Room
49 Staff
50 Officer-in-Charge
51 Staff
52 Draughtsmen and Clerical Staff

JOINT INTELLIGENCE COMMITTEE
54 JIC Director's Bedroom
55 Senior Mea Representative
56 JIC
57 Senior JIB Representative
58 Director GCHQ
59 Senior Service Representatives
61 Staff
64 JIC Sleeping Accommodation

JOINT PLANNING STAFF SECRETARIAT
60 Planning Staff
70 Deputy / Assistant Secretary
71 Clerical Staff

LIAISON
72 CIA / JIC Ottawa Representative

Above: The War Cabinet conference room, with the chairs still stacked in their original brown paper wrapping.

Below: The Prime Minister's map room. Below the mezzanine window there would have been a map table showing the state of the nation including the location of bomb drops, direction of fallout clouds and refugee movements, surviving airfields and other military infrastructure etc.

Above: The Lamson Tube exchange, a system of pneumatic tubes connecting the most important and most secure offices, by means of which sensitive documents could be exchanged without risk of interception.

Left: The bunker's public address system, installed in the aeroplane engine works to relay moral-boosting music and messages around the factory, it was re-used to perform a similar purpose in the bunker.

Above: One half of the headquarters' BBC broadcasting studio, from which instructions and moral-boosting messages could be broadcast to the nation. The transmitter equipment was not on-site, the broadcasts being relayed via cable to a remote BBC site, probably the BBC's own bunker at Wood Norton.

Below: two of four Mirrlees JVSS12 emergency alternator sets in the powerhouse in Area 11.

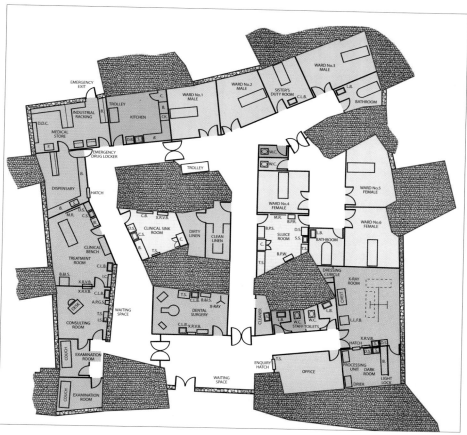

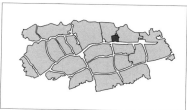

The Underground Hospital

Situated on East Main Road between the Stores and the Ministry of Transport area, the hospital included six female wards, three male wards, consulting rooms, a dentists room, an x-ray room, a dispensary, a kitchen and various sundry stores etc.

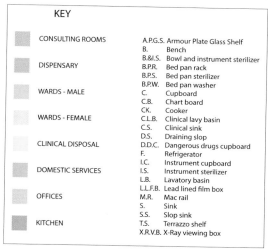

KEY

CONSULTING ROOMS

DISPENSARY

WARDS - MALE

WARDS - FEMALE

CLINICAL DISPOSAL

DOMESTIC SERVICES

OFFICES

KITCHEN

A.P.G.S.	Armour Plate Glass Shelf
B.	Bench
B.&I.S.	Bowl and instrument sterilizer
B.P.R.	Bed pan rack
B.P.S.	Bed pan sterilizer
B.P.W.	Bed pan washer
C.	Cupboard
C.B.	Chart board
CK.	Cooker
C.L.B.	Clinical lavy basin
C.S.	Clinical sink
D.S.	Draining slop
D.D.C.	Dangerous drugs cupboard
F.	Refrigerator
I.C.	Instrument cupboard
I.S.	Instrument sterilizer
L.B.	Lavatory basin
L.L.F.B.	Lead lined film box
M.R.	Mac rail
S.	Sink
S.S.	Slop sink
T.S.	Terrazzo shelf
X.R.V.B.	X-Ray viewing box

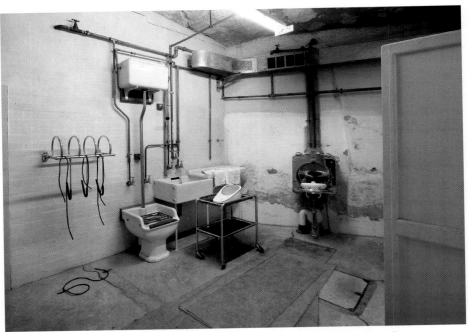

Above: The hospital sluice room, with some sinister looking implements hanging on the wall....

Below: The hospital reception area. The dentist's surgery is the first door on the left and the X-Ray department is at the far end of the corridor.

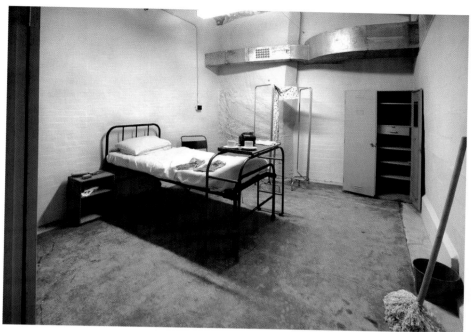

Above: Male ward No.1, with a couple of red rubber hot water bottles in their sealed bags.
Below: The Duty Nurse's office.

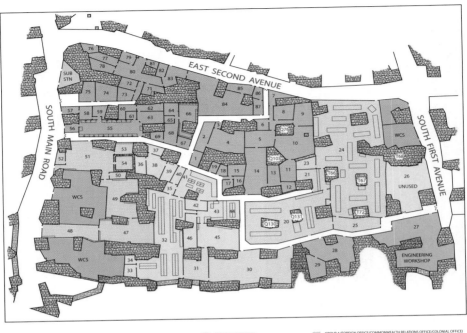

GROUP 3 (AIR MINISTRY)
RAF Signal Centre
57 RAF CO
61 Duty Signal Master
58 WO & Orderly Room
63 Traffic Office
53 Traffic Hall
59 Crypto Workshop
60 Crypto Equipment Room
Registry Telegrams
69 Head of Registry Telegrams
68 Head of Watch
65 Distribution
67 Message Reception
66 Off-Line Crypto
70 Line Relay Room
64 In and Out Hatches
62 Checking & Filing Office
56 Cloaks

REST ROOMS
28 -29   PO & Group 5 Joint Rest Rooms

GROUP 1 (WAR CABINET)
19 Chief Signal Officer
18 Duty Signal Staff Officers
1 Tube Exchange
War Cabinet Communications Office
16 Head of Office & Assistant to Head of Office
15 Chief of Cypher Office, Signal Officer
& Custodian & Supply Officer
17 Staff Clerical Officer & Office Clerks
5 Cypher Office
14 Teleprinter Room
10 Apparatus Room
9 Teleprinter Conference Room A
8 Teleprinter Conference Room B
6 Telephone Secrecy Room
4 Message Centre & Officer-in-Charge
3 Messenger's Lobby
2 Typing & Duplicating Room
12 Strong Room
11 Battery Room
13 Special Store Room
7 Store Room

GROUP 2 (ADMIRALTY)
79 Officer-in-Charge
82 Duty Signal Officer
74 Top Secret Crypto Officer
72 Crypto Officer
73 Crypto workshop
80 Main Signal Office
84 A/T Room
87 T/P Conference room
83 Routing room
71,88   Message & filing room
81 Messengers
75 On line cypher room
76 Stationery store
77 Perforating room
78 Duplicating room
85 Workshop & Ready Use Store
86 Equipment Room

GROUP 4 (FOREIGN OFFICE/COMMONWEALTH RELATIONS OFFICE/COLONIAL OFFICE)
50 Chief Signals Officer
51 Message Centre
48 Teleprinter Room
47 Machine Cypher Room
49 Book Cypher Room
53 Wireless Room
52 Typist

GROUP 5 (WAR OFFICE/HOME OFFICE & CIVIL DEPARTMENTS)
Message Centre
37 Head of Message Centre
36 Scrutiny Section
38 Classified & Unclassified Section
39 Distribution & Reproduction & Group 5 Pneumatic Tubes
Signal Centre
35 Chief Duty Signal Officer
40 Chief Duty Signal Officer-Clerks & Statistics & Records
41 Counter Room & Counter Room Supervisor
42 File and Re-Run Section
32 Traffic Hall , Out Traffic Supervisor, In Traffic Supervisor & Patching Panel
33 Teleprinter Switchboard Room
34 Apparatus Room
46 Chief Cypher Officer
43 Off-Line Cypher
45 Off-Line Cypher & Workshop
44 Stationery

COMMON USER
GPO Traffic Control
25 Officer-in-Charge & Enquiries
20,24   Teleprinters
21 Messenger Waiting Room
23 Store
30 Overseas Telephone & Telegraph
Control Equipment
31 Post Office

AREA 21 - Comms Centre

Area 21 housed the government
communication centre, more-or-less
equivalent to today's GCHQ. The centre
maintained direct cable links to military
establishments, embassies, allied powers
and other diplomatic facilities throughout
the world. The centre included hundreds of
teleprinters, tape readers, cypher machines etc,
and a large workshop to maintain them all.

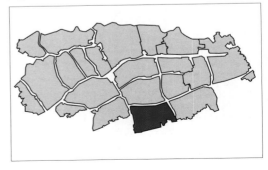

Above: Room 24, the common user teleprinter room in the communications centre.

Below: In the foreground, a Creed Type 7 teleprinter, one of over 700 such machines in the centre.

Above: Hundreds of teleprinter operators' chairs, still in their manufacturers' wrappings, stacked in the communication centre, ready for distribution to their allocated places..

Below: On the left of the desk is a Creed 6S tape reader/transmitter, to its right a Creed Type 7 teleprinter and right again a Type 45 off-line perforator.

Above: Room No.30 in the communications centre, the GPO overseas telephone and telegraph control equipment room.
Below: Racks of Voice Frequency Modulators in the GPO equipment room, necessary to convert the output from the teleprinters to voice frequency in the speech band to allow very long distance transmission.

225

Above: The teleprinter stores and maintenance section. The high level of humidity in this area has caused the wooden benching to decay and partially collapse.

Left: This is room 14, the War Cabinet Group No.1 teleprinter room, in the communication centre. The three instruments fitted with red and green lamps are teleprinter control instruments, the lamps indicating whether the lines are free, or in use for incoming or outgoing messages.

Above: The Sulzer air-conditioning plant in Area No.1 at the west end of the bunker; a similar plant was installed at the east end. These units were essential in the maintenance of an optimum level of humidity throughout the headquarters, and the difficulty in obtaining spare parts in the later years of its life contributed to the decision to decommission the site.

Below: Chlorine dosing tanks in the water treatment plant in Area No.11.

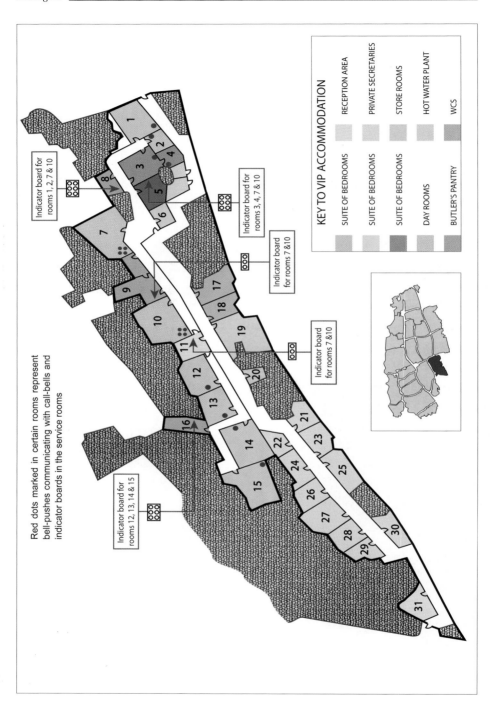

Area 17 - United Kingdom Land Forces & The V.I.P Section

The greater part of Area No.17, near the south-west corner of the Emergency Government War Headquarters, was allocated to the various functions of the United Kingdom Land Forces organisation, involved primarily with transport, supply and storage of vital military equipment, medical equipment, etc., together with personnel administration and the administration of military law through the department of the Judge Advocate General. Offices in this area were also occupied by staff of the Ministry of Aviation, including those responsible for civil aviation, the supply of civil and military aircraft and of guided weapons, as well as accommodation for the Ministry's Chief Scientist and his staff. Also housed in this section was the Ministry of Labour as well as, perhaps strangely, representatives of the British Employers Confederation and of the Trades Union Congress.

A small, isolate section towards the south of the area, however, performed a far different function, for this was designed to house the Royal Family and their staffs of servants and private secretaries. The first reference to the planning of this accommodation is in a hand-written note amongst a file of Cabinet Office papers from 1959, suggesting that it should be possible to house a Royal Party of up to twenty-five members, including staff, in the Central Government War Headquarters then under construction. Thereafter there is frustratingly little information available in the written records, other than a confirmation in 1961 that '*in the event of a crisis, the Queen would accompany her government*', which implies that at that time it was still intended that the Royal Family would decamp to Corsham. By 1964, however, when the utility of the Corsham bunker was already in doubt, an alternative plan for safeguarding the Royals, code-named operation *Candid,* suggests that the Royal Family might instead be dispersed to various country houses, rather like the country's art treasures at the start of the Second World War. Intriguingly, a document prepared in the early 1980s in connection with operation *Albatross* suggests that the special accommodation in Area 17 might be used for a group of eight V.V.I.Ps (Very, Very Important People) accompanied by ten personal secretaries, which would be a perfect fit for the Royal Family and their staff.

The accommodation, as can be seen from the plan, consists of an inner sanctum of sixteen rooms, accessible only via a security guardroom, together with an outer suite of rooms occupied by the private secretaries. All the Royal chambers are in communication with the service and security rooms via bell-pushes and indicators.

Below: Room No.11, the security guard room. The quarters for the Senior Royals are at the end of the darkened corridor to the right. Note the call-indicator board to the left of the clock.

Above: Bedroom No.3 in the royal suite, with bathroom beyond. There are servant's call buttons in both rooms.

Below: Room No.5, the en-suite bathroom attached to bedroom No.3 seen above. All the accommodation in the royal suite is surprisingly Spartan.